curriculum mathematics practice **6**

C Oliver   **A Ledsham**   **R Elvin**   **M Bindley**

Oxford University Press

OXFORD
UNIVERSITY PRESS

Great Clarendon Street, Oxford OX2 6DP

Oxford University Press is a department of the University of Oxford.
It furthers the University's objective of excellence in research,
scholarship, and education by publishing worldwide in

Oxford   New York

Auckland   Bangkok   Buenos Aires   Cape Town   Chennai
Dar es Salaam   Delhi   Hong Kong   Istanbul   Karachi   Kolkata
Kuala Lumpur   Madrid   Melbourne   Mexico City   Mumbai   Nairobi
São Paulo   Shanghai   Taipei   Tokyo   Toronto

Oxford is a registered trade mark of Oxford University Press
in the UK and in certain other countries

© Oxford University Press 1996

Series first published as *Comprehensive Mathematics Practice* 1981
Updated edition of *Curriculum Mathematics Practice* first published 1996
10   9   8   7   6   5

ISBN 0 19 833746 9
A CIP record for this book is available from the British Library.

Typeset and illustrated by Tech-Set Ltd
Printed and bound in Great Britain by Bell & Bain Ltd, Glasgow

Preface

Curriculum Mathematics Practice is an updated version of *Comprehensive Mathematics Practice*, a successful series designed for the majority of students in their first years of secondary schooling. As before, the books provide a vast range of carefully constructed and graded exercises in a coherent mathematical progression, with many of these exercises set in a real-life context. The levels targeted are 3–8, and details of how all six new books relate to the curriculum are given in the Answer Book.

These new books do not attempt to provide a complete scheme for the National Curriculum. No attempt has been made for instance to cover 'Using and Applying Mathematics' or computer work. It is expected, however, that mathematics departments will use other resources for those aspects (e.g. *Oxford Mathematics*) and that *Curriculum Mathematics Practice* will provide a core of skill practice within an overall scheme of work.

The series has the same objective as the original books. The series should enable students 'to gain confidence in their abilities and master the fundamental processes so necessary for future success'.

Mark Bindley
Revising Editor
December 1995

Contents

Unit 1 Powers

$2 \times 2 \times 2 \times 2 \times 2 = 2^5$ This is read as 2 to the power 5.

$3 \times 3 \times 3 \times 3 = 3^4$ This is read as 3 to the power 4.

$a \times a \times a \times a \times a \times a = a^6$ This is read as a to the power 6.

In the term 2^5, the figure 5 is called the *index*. The plural of index is *indices*.

Example 1

Find the value of the following.

a 5^3 **b** 10^4 **c** $3^2 \times 2^2$ **d** $2^5 \div 2^3$

a $5^3 = 5 \times 5 \times 5 = 25 \times 5 = 125$

b $10^4 = 10 \times 10 \times 10 \times 10 = 10\,000$

c $3^2 \times 2^2 = 3 \times 3 \times 2 \times 2 = 36$

d $2^5 \div 2^3 = \dfrac{2^5}{2^3} = \dfrac{2 \times 2 \times \cancel{2}^1 \times \cancel{2}^1 \times \cancel{2}^1}{\cancel{2}_1 \times \cancel{2}_1 \times \cancel{2}_1} = \dfrac{2 \times 2}{1} = \dfrac{4}{1} = 4$

Exercise 1.1

Find the value of the following.

1 5^2	**2** 3^2	**3** 10^2
4 4^2	**5** 4^3	**6** 2^3
7 3^3	**8** 10^3	**9** 2^4
10 3^4	**11** 5^4	**12** 2^5
13 10^5	**14** $3^2 \times 2^3$	**15** $4^2 \times 2^3$
16 $4^2 \times 2^2$	**17** $4^2 \times 3^2$	**18** $5^2 \times 2^2$
19 $5^2 \times 2^3$	**20** $5^2 \times 3^2$	**21** $10^2 \times 2^2$
22 $10^2 \times 2^4$	**23** $10^2 \times 2^5$	**24** $10^2 \times 3^2$
25 $10^2 \times 3^3$	**26** $10^2 \times 4^2$	**27** $10^2 \times 5^2$
28 $10^2 \times 5^3$	**29** $3^3 \times 2^2$	**30** $3^3 \times 2^3$
31 $4^3 \times 2^2$	**32** $4^3 \times 2^3$	**33** $4^3 \times 3^2$
34 $5^3 \times 2^2$	**35** $5^3 \times 3^2$	**36** $10^3 \times 2^2$
37 $10^3 \times 2^4$	**38** $10^3 \times 2^5$	**39** $10^3 \times 3^2$
40 $10^3 \times 3^3$	**41** $10^3 \times 4^2$	**42** $10^3 \times 5^2$
43 $3^4 \times 2^2$	**44** $3^4 \times 2^3$	**45** $10^4 \times 2^2$
46 $10^4 \times 2^5$	**47** $10^4 \times 3^2$	**48** $10^4 \times 3^3$
49 $4^2 \div 2^2$	**50** $4^2 \div 2^3$	**51** $4^2 \div 2$
52 $4^2 \div 2^4$	**53** $10^2 \div 2^2$	**54** $10^2 \div 5^2$
55 $10^2 \div 5$	**56** $4^3 \div 2^2$	**57** $4^3 \div 2^4$
58 $4^3 \div 2^5$	**59** $10^3 \div 2^2$	**60** $10^3 \div 2^3$
61 $10^3 \div 5^2$	**62** $10^3 \div 5^3$	**63** $10^3 \div 5$
64 $2^3 \div 4$	**65** $2^4 \div 4^2$	**66** $3^5 \div 3^2$
67 $3^5 \div 3^3$	**68** $3^5 \div 3^4$	**69** $3^5 \div 3$
70 $5^5 \div 5^2$	**71** $5^5 \div 5^3$	**72** $5^5 \div 5$
73 $10^5 \div 10^3$	**74** $10^5 \div 10^4$	**75** $3^4 \div 3^2$
76 $3^4 \div 3$	**77** $5^4 \div 5^2$	**78** $5^4 \div 5^3$
79 $5^3 \div 5$	**80** $4^3 \div 4^2$	**81** $4^3 \div 4$

Example 2

Simplify the following.

a $m \times m \times m \times m$ **b** $n^2 \times n^3$ **c** $2p \times 3p$

a $m \times m \times m \times m = m^4$

b $n^2 \times n^3 = n \times n \times n \times n \times n = n^5$

c $2p \times 3p = 2 \times p \times 3 \times p$
$$= 2 \times 3 \times p \times p$$
$$= 6p^2$$

Exercise 1.2

Simplify the following.

1 $a \times a \times a$	**2** $b \times b \times b \times b \times b$	**3** $c \times c$
4 $d \times d \times d \times d \times d \times d$	**5** $e \times e \times e \times e \times e \times e$	**6** $p^3 \times p^2$
7 $2q^3 \times q^2$	**8** $r^3 \times 4r^2$	**9** $5s^3 \times 2s^2$
10 $t^3 \times t^3$	**11** $7u^3 \times u^3$	**12** $4v^3 \times 3v^3$
13 $a^3 \times a$	**14** $6b^3 \times b$	**15** $3c^3 \times 8c$
16 $m^4 \times m^3$	**17** $n^4 \times 8n^3$	**18** $5p^4 \times 4p^3$
19 $d^4 \times d^2$	**20** $4e^4 \times e^2$	**21** $2f^4 \times 9f^2$
22 $s^4 \times s$	**23** $u^4 \times 6u$	**24** $7v^4 \times 5v$
25 $a^5 \times a^2$	**26** $12c^5 \times c^2$	**27** $8d^5 \times 2d^2$
28 $p^5 \times p$	**29** $11q^5 \times q$	**30** $15r^5 \times 2r$
31 $t^2 \times t^2$	**32** $u^2 \times 5u^2$	**33** $4v^2 \times 7v^2$
34 $m^2 \times m$	**35** $9n^2 \times n$	**36** $p^2 \times 11p$
37 $8q^2 \times 5q$	**38** $4d \times 5d$	**39** $5e \times e$
40 $f \times 12f$		

Example 3

Simplify the following.

a $y^5 \div y^3$ **b** $a^4 \div a^4$ **c** $8m^4 \div 4m^3$

a $y^5 \div y^3 = \dfrac{y^5}{y^3} = \dfrac{y \times y \times \cancel{y}^{1} \times \cancel{y}^{1} \times \cancel{y}^{1}}{\cancel{y}_{1} \times \cancel{y}_{1} \times \cancel{y}_{1}} = \dfrac{y \times y}{1} = y^2$

b $a^4 \div a^4 = \dfrac{a^4}{a^4} = \dfrac{\cancel{a}^{1} \times \cancel{a}^{1} \times \cancel{a}^{1} \times \cancel{a}^{1}}{\cancel{a}_{1} \times \cancel{a}_{1} \times \cancel{a}_{1} \times \cancel{a}_{1}} = 1$

c $8m^4 \div 4m^3 = \dfrac{8m^4}{4m^3} = \dfrac{\cancel{8}^{2} \times m \times \cancel{m}^{1} \times \cancel{m}^{1} \times \cancel{m}^{1}}{\cancel{4}_{1} \times \cancel{m}_{1} \times \cancel{m}_{1} \times \cancel{m}_{1}} = \dfrac{2m}{1} = 2m$

Exercise 1.3

Simplify the following.

1 $a^7 \div a^5$
2 $5b^7 \div b^5$
3 $8c^7 \div 2c^5$
4 $p^7 \div p^4$
5 $3q^7 \div q^4$
6 $12r^7 \div 6r^4$
7 $t^7 \div t^3$
8 $4u^7 \div u^3$
9 $9v^7 \div 3v^3$
10 $m^7 \div m^2$
11 $15n^7 \div 3n^2$
12 $a^6 \div a^4$
13 $8b^6 \div b^4$
14 $16c^6 \div 4c^4$
15 $d^6 \div d^3$
16 $11e^6 \div e^3$
17 $8f^6 \div 4f^3$
18 $y^6 \div y^2$
19 $20z^6 \div 5z^2$
20 $p^5 \div p^3$
21 $7q^5 \div q^3$
22 $14r^5 \div 2r^3$
23 $m^5 \div m^2$
24 $30n^5 \div 5n^2$
25 $t^5 \div t^4$
26 $6u^5 \div u^4$
27 $15v^5 \div 5v^4$
28 $p^5 \div p$
29 $9q^5 \div q$
30 $18r^5 \div 6r$
31 $a^4 \div a^2$
32 $4b^4 \div b^2$
33 $25c^4 \div 5c^2$
34 $r^4 \div r^3$
35 $10s^4 \div s^3$
36 $20t^4 \div 4t^3$
37 $m^4 \div m^4$
38 $6n^4 \div n^4$
39 $24p^4 \div 8p^4$
40 $t^3 \div t$
41 $8u^3 \div u$
42 $21v^3 \div 7v$
43 $b^3 \div b^3$
44 $13c^3 \div c^3$
45 $16d^3 \div 2d^3$
46 $p^2 \div p$
47 $9q^2 \div q$
48 $30r^2 \div 6r$
49 $y^2 \div y^2$
50 $24z^2 \div 3z^2$

Standard form

To multiply a number by 10, move the figures one place to the left.

e.g. $26 \times 10 = 260$

To multiply a number by 100, move the figures two places to the left.

e.g. $3.632 \times 100 = 363.2$

To divide a number by 10, move the figures one place to the right.

e.g. $26 \div 10 = 2.6$

To divide a number by 100, move the figures two places to the right.

e.g. $3.63 \div 100 = 0.0363$

Exercise 1.4

For questions 1 to 11, multiply each number by 10.

1 5
2 7
3 28
4 80
5 3.43
6 2.59
7 5.481
8 2.507
9 6.2
10 5.4
11 0.6

For questions 12 to 22, multiply each number by 100.

12 4
13 9
14 18
15 90
16 7.238
17 5.001
18 2.45
19 8.13
20 0.76
21 5.3
22 7.2

For questions 23 to 33, multiply each number by 1000.

23 3
24 8
25 52
26 70
27 5.431
28 7.005
29 0.842
30 4.35
31 6.27
32 6.7
33 0.4

For questions 34 to 46, divide each number by 10.

34 324
35 917
36 570
37 48
38 37
39 60
40 453.6
41 530.7
42 36.27
43 80.05
44 4.81
45 2.8
46 0.43

For questions 47 to 61, divide each number by 100.

47 2548
48 7820
49 8400
50 631
51 302
52 850
53 700
54 57
55 25
56 739.5
57 403.2
58 56.07
59 30.6
60 5.34
61 8.29

For questions 62 to 70, divide each number by 1000.

62 3724
63 4210
64 2500
65 853
66 270
67 400
68 35
69 52
70 40

The number 426 can be written as

$$4.26 \times 100 \quad \text{or} \quad \underline{4.26 \times 10^2}$$

The number 1735 can be written as

$$1.735 \times 100 \quad \text{or} \quad \underline{1.735 \times 10^3}$$

The underlined numbers are written in *standard form* (sometimes called scientific notation). Standard form is a useful way of writing down very large numbers that include a lot of noughts.

e.g. $15\,000\,000 = 1.5 \times 10^7$

A number in standard form is a number between 1 and 10, multiplied by a power of ten.

Example 4

Write the following in standard form.

a 36
b 256
c 1860

a $36 = 3.6 \times 10 = 3.6 \times 10^1$

b $256 = 2.56 \times 100 = 2.56 \times 10^2$

c $1860 = 1.86 \times 1000 = 1.86 \times 10^3$

4

Exercise 1.5

Write in standard form.

1 1754	**2** 2139	**3** 5627	**4** 4071
5 3480	**6** 1920	**7** 2500	**8** 3900
9 5000	**10** 8000	**11** 372	**12** 916
13 495	**14** 109	**15** 260	**16** 580
17 600	**18** 900	**19** 271.4	**20** 532.7
21 804.5	**22** 300.9	**23** 45	**24** 91
25 70	**26** 40	**27** 37.3	**28** 70.6
29 24.52	**30** 50.39		

Example 5

Find the number to replace the □ in the following.

a $\square = 7.26 \times 10^1$ **b** $\square = 4.23 \times 10^3$
c $34.9 = 3.49 \times \square$ **d** $172 = \square \times 10^2$

a $\square = 7.26 \times 10^1$, so $\square = 72.6$

b $\square = 4.23 \times 10^3$
$= 4.23 \times 1000 = 4230$

c $34.9 = 3.49 \times \square$, so $\square = 10^1 = 10$
because $3.49 \times 10 = 34.9$

d $172 = \square \times 10^2 = \square \times 100$
so $\square = 1.72$
because $1.72 \times 100 = 172$

Exercise 1.6

Find the number to replace the □ in each of the following.

1 $\square = 5.372 \times 10^1$	**2** $\square = 2.561 \times 10^1$
3 $\square = 1.39 \times 10^1$	**4** $\square = 4.5 \times 10^1$
5 $\square = 4.165 \times 10^2$	**6** $\square = 3.56 \times 10^2$
7 $\square = 6.3 \times 10^2$	**8** $\square = 2.425 \times 10^3$
9 $\square = 8.54 \times 10^3$	**10** $\square = 7.8 \times 10^3$
11 $53.24 = 5.324 \times \square$	**12** $28.5 = 2.85 \times \square$
13 $48 = 4.8 \times \square$	**14** $674.2 = 6.742 \times \square$
15 $308.5 = 3.085 \times \square$	**16** $729 = 7.29 \times \square$
17 $680 = 6.8 \times \square$	**18** $1532 = 1.532 \times \square$
19 $4250 = 4.25 \times \square$	**20** $9300 = 9.3 \times \square$
21 $35.12 = \square \times 10^1$	**22** $53.4 = \square \times 10^1$
23 $65 = \square \times 10^1$	**24** $432.6 = \square \times 10^2$
25 $537 = \square \times 10^2$	**26** $840 = \square \times 10^2$
27 $2415 = \square \times 10^3$	**28** $3570 = \square \times 10^3$
29 $6400 = \square \times 10^3$	**30** $7000 = \square \times 10^3$

Example 6

Change the following into ordinary numbers.

a 3.06×10^2 **b** 9.84×10^3

a $3.06 \times 10^2 = 3.06 \times 100 = 306$

b $9.84 \times 10^3 = 9.84 \times 1000 = 9840$

Exercise 1.7

Change the following into ordinary numbers.

1 1.936×10^3	**2** 4.572×10^3
3 8.126×10^3	**4** 5.093×10^3
5 2.73×10^3	**6** 9.15×10^3
7 6.8×10^3	**8** 7.4×10^3
9 2×10^3	**10** 7×10^3
11 9.32×10^2	**12** 1.56×10^2
13 8.19×10^2	**14** 4.05×10^2
15 6.3×10^2	**16** 4.9×10^2
17 3×10^2	**18** 5×10^2
19 5.316×10^2	**20** 4.951×10^2
21 1.075×10^2	**22** 6.104×10^2
23 6.7×10^1	**24** 8.4×10^1
25 8×10^1	**26** 6×10^1
27 5.53×10^1	**28** 1.05×10^1
29 9.436×10^1	**30** 8.005×10^1

Example 7

Work out the following, leaving the answers in standard form.

a $2.0 \times 10^2 \times 3.0 \times 10^1$
b $4.0 \times 10^1 \times 6.0 \times 10^2$

a $2.0 \times 10^2 \times 3.0 \times 10^1$
$= 2.0 \times 3.0 \times 10^2 \times 10^1$
$= 2.0 \times 3.0 \times 10 \times 10 \times 10$
$= 6.0 \times 10^3$

b $4.0 \times 10^1 \times 6.0 \times 10^2$
$= 4.0 \times 6.0 \times 10^1 \times 10^2$
$= 4.0 \times 6.0 \times 10 \times 10 \times 10$
$= 24.0 \times 10 \times 10 \times 10$
$= 2.4 \times 10 \times 10 \times 10 \times 10$
$= 2.4 \times 10^4$

Exercise 1.8

Work out the following, leaving the answers in standard form.

1 $4.0 \times 10^2 \times 2.0 \times 10^1$
2 $3.0 \times 10^2 \times 3.0 \times 10^1$
3 $2.0 \times 10^2 \times 2.0 \times 10$
4 $1.2 \times 10^2 \times 5.0 \times 10$
5 $2.5 \times 10^2 \times 2.0 \times 10$
6 $1.5 \times 10 \times 4.0 \times 10^2$
7 $3.5 \times 10 \times 2.0 \times 10^2$
8 $2.5 \times 10^1 \times 2.0 \times 10^1$
9 $4.5 \times 10^1 \times 2.0 \times 10^1$
10 $1.5 \times 10 \times 6.0 \times 10$
11 $7.0 \times 10 \times 2.0 \times 10$
12 $5.0 \times 10 \times 3.0 \times 10$
13 $6.0 \times 10 \times 4.0 \times 10$
14 $4.0 \times 10 \times 5.0 \times 10$
15 $5.0 \times 10 \times 6.0 \times 10$
16 $8.0 \times 10 \times 3.0 \times 10^2$
17 $9.0 \times 10 \times 4.0 \times 10^2$
18 $7.0 \times 10 \times 7.0 \times 10^2$
19 $6.0 \times 10 \times 8.0 \times 10^2$
20 $8.0 \times 10 \times 5.0 \times 10^2$

Very large calculations like $345\,000 \times 789\,000$ produce answers which do not fit on a calculator display.

Simple calculators cannot perform these calculations and show an error message.

Scientific calculators display the answers in the standard form. If $345\,000 \times 789\,000$ is entered on a scientific calculator the answer is given as

$$2.72205\,\text{E}11$$

$2.72205\,\text{E}11$ means 2.72205×10^{11}

$2.72205 \times 10^{11} = 272\,205\,000\,000$

Exercise 1.9

Write each of these answers from a scientific calculator as an ordinary number.

1 5.6780
2 5.8781
3 5.6782
4 1.50885
5 9.3281
6 2.670986
7 3.4580
8 3.4581
9 3.4582
10 3.4583
11 3.4584
12 4.8185661
13 8.1182980
14 1.3016114482
15 2.662333809
16 1.44115981
17 4.727839568
18 1.844614469
19 1.04603580
20 7.831098580

Compound interest

A scientific calculator will have a button specifically for powers. It will probably be marked like this.

Example 8

Use a scientific calculator to find the value of the following.

a 7^9
b 15^{12}

a 7 x^y 9 = 40353607
b 15 x^y 12 = 1.297463464

$= 129\,746\,340\,000\,000$

Exercise 1.10

Use a scientific calculator to find the value of the following.

1 4^7
2 14^5
3 17^7
4 8^{11}
5 12^9
6 1.5^5
7 1.1^8
8 1.15^7
9 1.3^{20}
10 1.4^{25}
11 7^8
12 49^4
13 0.95^6
14 0.9^{15}
15 0.85^{20}
16 0.8^{99}
17 0.81^{13}
18 2^{24}
19 4^{12}
20 8^8
21 16^3
22 25^{12}
23 125^8
24 99^9

Eight years ago, Mrs Jones invested £1000 in a Building Society account paying 5% interest per year. She has not withdrawn any money and has allowed the interest each year to be added to the total in her account.

We can calculate the total she now has in her account like this.

After one year, the total is £1000 plus 5%, or

$$105\% \text{ of } £1000 = 1000 \div 100 \times 105$$
$$= 1000 \times 1.05$$
$$= £1050$$

After two years the total is £1050 plus 5%, or

$$105\% \text{ of } £1050 = 1050 \div 100 \times 105$$
$$= 1050 \times 1.05$$
$$= £1120.50$$

Each year, the new total will be found by multiplying the old total by 1.05, so after 8 years the total in Mrs Jones's account will be

$$£1000 \times 1.05^8 = 1000 \times 1.477\,455\,4$$
$$= £1477.46 \text{ (to the nearest penny)}$$

Investing money like this and allowing the interest to accumulate is called investing with *compound interest*.

Example 9

a What is the final value of £5000 after being invested for 10 years at a rate of compound interest of 8%?

An increase of 8% is equivalent to a multiplication by 1.08.

So after 10 years the final value is

$$5000 \times 1.08^{10} = 5000 \times 2.158\,925$$
$$= £10\,794.63 \text{ (to the nearest penny)}$$

b If prices are increasing by 10% a year, what will a bottle of milk, which now costs 46 p, cost in 50 years' time?

An increase of 10% is equivalent to a multiplication by 1.1.

So after 50 years the bottle of milk will cost

$$46 \times 1.1^{50} = 46 \times 117.390\,85$$
$$= 5400\,p \text{ (to the nearest penny)}$$
$$= £54$$

c If prices are increasing by 10% a year, write a formula for the cost in *n* years' time of a bottle of milk which now costs 46 p.

A formula for the cost after *n* years is

$$\text{cost} = 46\,p \times 1.1^n$$

Exercise 1.11

1 A building society offers a special account paying 7% compound interest per year.

Special Platinum Account
offers 7% interest per year

Find the final value of the following amounts invested for the times given.
a £5000 invested for 6 years
b £800 invested for 11 years
c £12 500 invested for 8 years
d £1000 invested for 7 years
e £1000 invested for *n* years

2 The Government is worried because prices are rising by 3% a year.
What will the following items cost in 10 years if prices continue to rise at this rate?
a A loaf of bread which costs 45 p
b A bottle of wine which costs £3.45
c A book which costs £15.60
d A car which costs £12 000
e A house which costs £85 000

3 A plant disease has already infected 2000 acres of crops and is spreading at a rate of 12% each year.

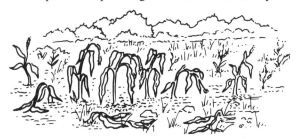

If this rate of increase continues, what acreage of crops will be infected after
a 5 years   **b** 6 years   **c** 10 years
d 20 years   **e** *n* years?

4 Vali discovered an old bank book in which her great-grandfather had invested £5 at a rate of compound interest of 4%.

What will the account be worth if it is the following number of years since the £5 was invested?
a 60 years   **b** 70 years   **c** 80 years
d 90 years   **e** 100 years

5 A survey shows the population of a town is 50 000 and increasing by 14% every year.
If this rate of increase continues, what will the population of the town be in
a 5 years **b** 6 years **c** 12 years
d 20 years **e** n years?

Example 10

A shop decides to reduce the price of all winter jackets by 5% every day until they are sold.
If a jacket costs £125 at the start of the sale, how much will it cost on

a day 1 **b** day 2 **c** day 5?

a On day 1 the coat will cost 95% of its previous value.

cost on day 1 = (£125 ÷ 100) × 95
= £125 × 0.95 = £118.75

A 5% reduction is equivalent to multiplying by 0.95.

b By day 2, the coat will have been reduced by 5% twice. So,

cost on day 2 = £125 × 0.95 × 0.95
= £112.81 (to the nearest penny)

c By day 5, the coat will have been reduced by 5% five times. So,

cost on day 5 = £125 × 0.95^5
= £125 × 0.773 780 9
= £96.72

Example 11

The population of Tekram is currently 20 000 but falling by 10% a year.
What will the population be in

a 1 year's time **b** 8 years' time **c** n years' time?

a Population in 1 year = (20 000 ÷ 100) × 90
= 20 000 × 0.9 = 18 000

A 10% reduction is equivalent to multiplying by 0.9.

b Population in 8 years = 20 000 × 0.9^8
= 20 000 × 0.430 467 2
= 8609 (to the nearest person)

c Population in n years = 20 000 × 0.9^n

Exercise 1.12

1 Sally has a car worth £6500 but finds that it is decreasing in value by 15% a year.
Find the value of Sally's car after
a 1 year **b** 2 years **c** 4 years **d** n years.

2 Trevor wants to sell a mountain bike. He advertises it like this:

> **Mountain Bike For Sale**
> Starting Price £110
> The price will be reduced by 2% every day until the bike is sold!

How much will the bike cost if it is bought after
a 1 day **b** 2 days **c** 5 days **d** n days?

3 A country's Minister of Agriculture estimates the country has 2 000 000 acres of rain forest but that 8% is being cut down every year.
If this rate of timber felling continues, how many acres of rain forest will remain in
a 1 year **b** 2 years **c** 4 years **d** n years?

4 An endangered species has a current population of 1000 in a certain area but this is being reduced by 12% every year.

If this reduction in numbers continues, how many animals will be left in
a 1 year **b** 3 years **c** 6 years **d** n years?

5 A weevil is killing 20% of the plants in a field every day.
If there are currently 22 000 plants in the field and this rate of decrease continues, how many plants will there be in
a 1 day **b** 4 days **c** 1 week **d** n days?

Unit 2 Algebra

This exercise revises negative numbers and substitution.

Exercise 2.1

In questions **1** to **20** find the 'odd answer out'.

1 a 8 add 7
  b 11 add 5
  c 20 add -5

2 a 12 add -7
  b 15 add -9
  c -14 add 20

3 a -2 add 10
  b -5 add 12
  c 25 take away 18

4 a 14 take away 6
  b 26 take away 19
  c 5 take away -3

5 a 6 take away -5
  b 9 take away -3
  c -3 take away -15

6 a -5 take away -20
  b -9 take away -24
  c 7 add 9

7 a -5 add -3
  b -7 add -2
  c 3 add -12

8 a 2 add -8
  b 10 add -15
  c -10 add 4

9 a -10 add 2
  b -12 add 5
  c 12 take away 20

10 a 3 take away 15
  b 13 take away 25
  c -6 take away 5

11 a -8 take away 6
  b -11 take away 4
  c -20 take away -5

12 a -15 take away -2
  b -19 take away -7
  c -7 add -5

13 a 6×4
  b 12×2
  c -9×-3

14 a -5×-4
  b -6×-3
  c $100 \div 5$

15 a $42 \div 7$
  b $40 \div 8$
  c $-54 \div -9$

16 a $-96 \div -6$
  b $-144 \div -8$
  c 9×2

17 a 15×-6
  b 18×-5
  c -23×4

18 a -24×3
  b -19×4
  c $-360 \div 5$

19 a $-104 \div 8$
  b $-135 \div 9$
  c $105 \div -7$

20 a $294 \div -7$
  b $220 \div -5$
  c 14×-3

If $a = 4$ and $b = 2$, find the value of

21 $3a + b$ **22** $a + 4b$ **23** $4a + b$
24 $4a + 3b$ **25** $2a + 5b$ **26** $5ab$
27 $9ab$ **28** $7a^2$ **29** $8b^2$
30 $a^2 + b^2$ **31** a^2b **32** $4a^2b$
33 ab^2 **34** $6ab^2$ **35** a^3
36 b^3 **37** $a^3 + b^3$ **38** $2a^3$
39 $2b^3$ **40** $5b^3$

If $p = 5$ and $q = 3$, find the value of

41 $2p - q$ **42** $5p - 3q$ **43** $3p - 4q$
44 $4p - 5q$ **45** $4pq$ **46** $7pq$
47 $6p^2$ **48** $5q^2$ **49** $p^2 - q^2$
50 p^2q **51** $2p^2q$ **52** $6p^2q$
53 pq^2 **54** $4pq^2$ **55** p^3
56 q^3 **57** $p^3 - q^3$ **58** $2p^3$
59 $4q^3$ **60** $10q^3$

If $a = 3$, $b = -2$, $c = -4$ and $d = 0$, find the value of

61 $3ab$ **62** $4bc$ **63** $5ac$
64 $4a \div b$ **65** $8a \div c$ **66** $6b \div c$
67 $3b \div a$ **68** $9c \div a$ **69** $10c \div b$
70 $4ab \div c$ **71** $2ac \div 6$ **72** $6bc \div a$
73 $2abc$ **74** $3abcd$ **75** $7abd \div c$

If $p = -2$, $q = -3$, $r = -6$ and $s = 0$, find the value of

76 $2pq$ **77** $4qr$ **78** $5pr$
79 $9p \div q$ **80** $18p \div r$ **81** $24q \div r$
82 $8q \div p$ **83** $12r \div p$ **84** $15r \div q$
85 $9pq \div r$ **86** $pr \div 2q$ **87** $qr \div 3p$
88 $3pqr$ **89** $12qs \div p$ **90** $ps \div 11rq$

91 Find (i) the area, (ii) the perimeter of the rectangle when the side dimensions have the values given below.

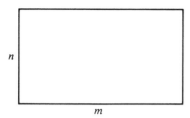

a $m = 24$ cm, $n = 6$ cm
b $m = 18$ cm, $n = 8$ cm
c $m = 16$ cm, $n = 9$ cm
d $m = 12$ cm, $n = 12$ cm
What do you notice about the areas of these four rectangles?
What is special about the rectangle with the smallest perimeter?

92 Find (i) the area, (ii) the perimeter of the right-angled triangle when the side dimensions have the values given below.

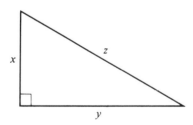

a $x = 3$ m, $y = 4$ m, $z = 5$ m
b $x = 5$ m, $y = 12$ m, $z = 13$ m
c $x = 8$ cm, $y = 15$ cm, $z = 17$ cm
d $x = 7$ cm, $y = 24$ cm, $z = 25$ cm
e $x = 20$ mm, $y = 21$ mm, $z = 29$ mm

A newspaper charges for advertisements using the rule

the cost is 80 p + 90 p per line

We can write this as the *formula*

$$C = 90L + 80$$

where C is the cost (in pence) and L is the number of lines.

Example 1

Find the cost of this advertisement.

> **COSTA BLANCA** Complex with pool, tennis, 2 beautiful villas slps 6 each. Tel 0354 840337.

There are 3 lines in the advertisement.

$$C = (3 \times 90) + 80$$
$$C = 350$$

The cost is £3.50.

Exercise 2.2

1 Find the cost of each of these advertisements, using the formula given in the example.

a
> **CHATEAUX.** Region of Loire. Designer's cottages with pools. Medieval town, walk shops. Golf/wine. 0579 796 515.

b
> **COTE D'AZUR.** Grasse very lovely stone mas in lge olive grove: 4–5 bedrms/4 bathrms; seaviews; Sat. TV: 50ft pool & poolhse; games rm; total peace & privacy. £950–£2950 pw. Tel 02034 98936885 fax 3904.

c
> **COTE D'AZUR.** Lovely old Mod Frmhse in 2 acre terraced olive grove, 20 mins coast nr Grasse 4 dbl bed, 2 bath, pool, views. 8th Jul-16th Sep £800-1200 pw inc Maid Service. 0324 773534.

d
> **FRANCE** Dordogne. Delightful converted barn in tranquil, listed hill village. Slps 8, 4 dble bdrms, 2 bthrms, lge pool, (safely fenced in), dishwasher and all mod cons. Phone us in Belgium 020 233 5336 57 33 and we'll call straight back, or fax 020 233 5336 07 67.

e
> **FREE DRINKS,** all Sports, Full Board at this House Party sporting holiday in the Dordogne. Tennis, Clay Pigeon Shooting, Badminton and Snooker etc. £270 pp pw. Nothing else to pay. Sorry most weeks no children. Phone Mandy 00425 621544 or John 0300 35 38 52 09.

2 The formula for the weight (W) in kg of a certain piglet is

$$W = 1.8 + 0.5D$$

where D is the number of days since the piglet was born.

a Find the weight of the piglet after
  (i) 3 days   (ii) 5 days   (iii) 25 days.
b How much did the piglet weigh when it was born?

3 The formula $S = 3L - 25$ links the foot length (L) measured in inches with the shoe size (S).
  a What size shoes fit feet of the following lengths?
    (i) 10 inches   (ii) 11 inches   (iii) $9\frac{1}{3}$ inches
    (iv) 12 inches   (v) $10\frac{2}{3}$ inches
  b John Thrupp of Stratford-upon-Avon has the biggest feet in England. They are $15\frac{1}{3}$ inches long.
    What size shoe does he wear?
  c The largest known feet in the world are those of Muhammad Adlam Channa of Pakistan. He wears a size 22 shoe.
    How long are his feet?
  d If they were made, how long would these shoes be?
    (i) size 0   (ii) size -1 (iii) size -10

4 The formula to convert a temperature measured in degrees Celsius (C) into a temperature measured in degrees Fahrenheit (F) is
$F = 9C/5 + 32$
  a Convert these Celsius temperatures into Fahrenheit.
    (i) $20\,°C$ (ii) $45\,°C$ (iii) $62\,°C$ (iv) $100\,°C$
  b Copy and complete this conversion table for Celsius to Fahrenheit.

°C	0	20	40	60	80	100	120	140	160	180	200	220
°F	32											

c A simple approximate formula to convert a temperature measured in degrees Celsius (C) into a temperature measured in degrees Fahrenheit (F) is $F = 2C + 30$
  (i) Make a conversion table using this formula.
  (ii) Does the accurate formula ever agree with the approximate formula?
  (iii) Do you think the approximate formula is accurate enough to use to convert cooking temperatures from Celsius to Fahrenheit?

5 The depth of a well (D) is linked with the time it takes a stone to drop to the bottom (T) by the formula $D = 5T^2$, where D is measured in metres and T is measured in seconds.
  a How deep is the well if a stone drops to the bottom in
    (i) 1 second   (ii) 1.5 seconds
    (iii) 2.5 seconds   (iv) 3.5 seconds?
  b How long will a stone take to drop in a well with a depth of
    (i) 45 metres   (ii) 20 metres
    (iii) 51.2 metres   (iv) 28.8 metres?

6 In Britain, stopping distances for cars are calculated using the formula

$$D = \frac{(S^2 + 20S)}{60}$$

where S is the speed of the car in miles per hour and D is the stopping distance in metres.

a Copy and complete this table for speed and stopping distance.

speed (mph)	0	10	20	30	40	50	60	70
stopping distance (metres)								

b In the Netherlands, the simpler rule

$$D = \frac{4S}{5}$$

is used, where S is the speed of the car in miles per hour and D is the stopping distance in metres.
Make a table for this formula.
c Which rule do you think is safer?

Changing the subject

$$A = LB; \qquad L = \frac{A}{B}; \qquad \frac{A}{L} = B$$

These are all arrangements of the same formula, but the subject of each is different. To change the subject of a formula, we use a similar method to that for solving an equation.

Example 2

a Make x the subject of $y = mx$

$$y = mx$$

$\Rightarrow \quad \dfrac{y}{m} = x$ (divide both sides by m)

b Rearrange $C = 2\pi r$ to find the value of r

$$C = 2\pi r$$

$\Rightarrow \quad \dfrac{C}{2\pi} = r$ (divide both sides by 2π)

Exercise 2.3

1 Make b the subject of $A = bh$
2 Rearrange $V = Al$ to find l
3 If $P = VI$, find the value of V
4 Transpose $v = lf$ to make f the subject
5 Make a the subject of $v = at$
6 If $q = It$, find the value of t
7 Transpose $U = Pt$ to make P the subject
8 Rearrange $F = ma$ to find a
9 $m = Zq$ Change the subject to Z
10 Make V the subject of $k = PV$
11 Find F when $W = Fd$
12 Rearrange $P = hdg$ to find d
13 If $I = PrT$, find the value of P
14 Transpose $W = mgh$ to make h the subject
15 Make b the subject of $V = lbh$
16 If $A = \pi Dl$, find the value of D
17 Rearrange $A = 4lb$ to find b
18 $S = 4bh$ Change the subject to b
19 Find l when $A = 3ls$
20 Make s the subject of $v^2 = 2as$

Example 3

a If $r = \dfrac{D}{2}$, find the value of D

$$r = \frac{D}{2}$$

$\Rightarrow \quad 2r = D$ (multiply both sides by 2)

b Find C when $\pi = \dfrac{C}{D}$

$$\pi = \frac{C}{D}$$

$\Rightarrow \quad \pi D = C$ (multiply both sides by D)

c Make H the subject of $A = \dfrac{BH}{2}$

$$A = \frac{BH}{2}$$

$\Rightarrow \quad 2A = BH$ (multiply both sides by 2)

$\dfrac{2A}{B} = H$ (divide both sides by B)

Exercise 2.4

1 Find x when $n = \dfrac{x}{y}$

2 Make V the subject of $R = \dfrac{V}{I}$

3 If $s = \dfrac{d}{t}$, find the value of d

4 Transpose $L = \dfrac{H}{m}$ to make H the subject

5 Rearrange $D = \dfrac{m}{v}$ to find m

6 Find v when $m = \dfrac{v}{u}$

7 $P = \dfrac{F}{A}$ Rearrange to find F

8 Make P the subject of $k = \dfrac{P}{T}$

9 If $c = \dfrac{V}{T}$, find the value of V

10 Find p when $l = \dfrac{p}{4}$

11 Rearrange $s = \dfrac{q}{3}$ to find q

12 Make r the subject of $b = \dfrac{r}{15}$

13 Find l when $L = \dfrac{l}{10}$

12

14 $W = \dfrac{D}{7}$ Rearrange to find D

15 Make M the subject of $Y = \dfrac{M}{12}$

16 If $h = \dfrac{m}{60}$, find the value of m

17 Transpose $D = \dfrac{h}{24}$ to find h

18 Find m when $M = \dfrac{m}{100}$

19 Make v the subject of $V = \dfrac{v}{1000}$

20 Rearrange $d = \dfrac{l}{50}$ to find l

21 Find **a** x, **b** y, when $m = \dfrac{xy}{10}$

22 Find **a** u, **b** v, when $a = \dfrac{uv}{50}$

23 If $t = \dfrac{pq}{25}$, find **a** p, **b** q

24 If $V = \dfrac{Ah}{3}$, find **a** A, **b** h

25 $R = \dfrac{PV}{T}$ Rearrange to find **a** P, **b** V

26 If $a = \dfrac{pqr}{5}$ make the subject **a** p, **b** q, **c** r

27 Find **a** x, **b** y, **c** z, when $t = \dfrac{xyz}{20}$

28 Find **a** b, **b** h, **c** l, when $V = \dfrac{bhl}{2}$

29 Rearrange $V = \dfrac{abh}{3}$ to find **a** a, **b** b, **c** h

30 $I = \dfrac{PRt}{100}$ Rearrange to find **a** P, **b** R, **c** t

Example 4

a Make a the subject when $a + b = 180°$

$$a + b = 180°$$
$$\Rightarrow \quad a = 180° - b$$
(subtract b from both sides)

b Find h when $H = bt + h$

$$H = bt + h$$
$$\Rightarrow \quad H - bt = h$$
(subtract bt from both sides)

c If $v - u = at$, find the value of v

$$v - u = at$$
$$\Rightarrow \quad v = at + u$$
(add u to both sides)

1 Make m the subject of $m + n = u$

2 Rearrange $p + q = z$ to find p

3 If $a + b = t$, find the value of a

4 Transpose $x + y = 360°$ to make y the subject

5 Make b the subject of $p = b + c$

6 If $n = u + v$, find the value of u

7 Transpose $90° = r + s$ to make s the subject

8 Rearrange $q - r = t$ to find q

9 $b - c = v$ Change the subject to b

10 Make y the subject of $y - z = m$

11 Find a when $x = a - b$

12 Rearrange $n = p - q$ to find p

13 If $z = d - e$, find the value of d

14 Transpose $a + bt = A$ to make a the subject

15 Make p the subject of $p + qz = P$

16 If $V = v + ct$, find the value of v

17 Rearrange $P = p + at$ to find p

18 $H = h + kd$. Change the subject to h

19 Find c when $y = mx + c$

20 Make V the subject of $E = rI + V$

21 If $180° = 2y + z$, find the value of z

22 Rearrange $m - nt = M$ to find m

23 Find u when $u - vh = U$

24 Transpose $H = h -- vt$ to make h the subject

25 Make k the subject of $S = k - mt$

Example 5

a Find a when $v = u + at$

$$v = u + at$$
$$\Rightarrow \quad v - u = at$$
(subtract u from both sides)

$$\Rightarrow \quad \frac{v - u}{t} = a$$
(divide both sides by t)

b Make L the subject of $P = 2L + 2B$

$$P = 2L + 2B$$
$$\Rightarrow \quad P - 2B = 2L$$
(subtract $2B$ from both sides)

$$\Rightarrow \quad \frac{P - 2B}{2} = L$$
(divide both sides by 2)

Exercise 2.6

1 Find m the subject of $p = q + mn$
2 Make x the subject of $a = b + xy$
3 Rearrange $E = V + rI$ to find r
4 If $y = mx + c$, find the value of m
5 Transpose $z = st + k$ to make s the subject
6 Make a the subject of $m = ab - n$
7 Find p if $r = pq - s$
8 If $c = d + 2r$, find the value of r
9 Transpose $x = y + 5t$ to make t the subject
10 Rearrange $p = 2s + b$ to find s
11 $360° = 3m + n$. Change the subject to m
12 Make t the subject of $u = 4t - v$
13 Find z when $a = 10z - b$
14 Rearrange $x = 2a + 3b$ to find **a** a, **b** b
15 If $y = 3m + 8n$, find the value of **a** m, **b** n
16 Find **a** w, **b** l, when $s = 8w + 4l$
17 Find **a** x, **b** y, when $900° = 5x + 2y$
18 If $p = 2l + \pi d$, find **a** l, **b** d
19 Make b the subject of $t = 4b - 5c$
20 Find p if $z = 6p - 7q$
21 If $a = 3b + mn$, make the subject **a** b, **b** m, **c** n
22 If $p = 5q + uv$, make the subject **a** q, **b** u, **c** v
23 Make v the subject of $u = 6v - xy$
24 Find **a** p, **b** q, when $m = pq - 4n$
25 Find **a** r, **b** s, when $c = rs - 9d$
26 **a** Make a the subject of the formula $v = u + at$ and work out the value of a if $v = 45$, $u = 15$ and $t = 3$.
   b Make t the subject of the formula $v = u + at$ and work out the value of t if $v = 12$, $u = 4$ and $a = 2$.
27 **a** Make r the subject of the formula $E = V + rI$ and work out the value of r if $E = 24$, $V = 9$ and $I = 5$.
   b Make I the subject of the formula $E = V + rI$ and work out the value of I if $E = 30$, $V = 14$ and $r = 8$.
28 **a** Make a the subject of the formula $c = ab - d$ and work out the value of a if $c = 27$, $d = 29$ and $b = 8$.
   b Make b the subject of the formula $c = ab - d$ and work out the value of b if $c = 65$, $d = 67$ and $a = 11$.
29 **a** Make m the subject of the formula $p = mn - q$ and work out the value of m if $p = 14\frac{1}{2}$, $q = 15\frac{1}{2}$ and $n = 6$.
   b Make n the subject of the formula $p = mn - q$ and work out the value of n if $p = 5\frac{1}{4}$, $q = 6\frac{3}{4}$ and $m = 3$.
30 Rearrange the formula $P = p + kt$ so that k is the subject and find the value of k if $P = 95$, $p = 70$ and $t = 100$.

Expanding formulae

Reminder
When removing brackets, multiply each term inside the bracket by the term outside.

Example 6

Remove the brackets to simplify the following.

a $2(x - y)$ **b** $a(b + 2)$ **c** $2a(a + 3)$

a $2(x - y) = 2x - 2y$

b $a(b + 2) = ab + 2a$

c $2a(a + 3) = 2a^2 + 6a$

Exercise 2.7

Remove the brackets to simplify the following.

1 $2(x + y)$ 2 $4(m + n)$ 3 $5(u + v)$
4 $3(a - b)$ 5 $6(p - q)$ 6 $4(y - z)$
7 $3(x + 2)$ 8 $4(t + 3)$ 9 $5(r + 1)$
10 $2(a - 6)$ 11 $6(b - 5)$ 12 $4(2 + m)$
13 $5(3 + n)$ 14 $3(8 - p)$ 15 $5(5 - q)$
16 $a(b + c)$ 17 $x(y + z)$ 18 $p(q - r)$
19 $b(c - d)$ 20 $m(m + n)$ 21 $u(u + v)$
22 $a(a - b)$ 23 $x(x - y)$ 24 $p(q - p)$
25 $d(e - d)$ 26 $m(n + 3)$ 27 $p(q + 5)$
28 $x(x + 2)$ 29 $t(t + 4)$ 30 $a(b - 6)$
31 $u(v - 1)$ 32 $z(z - 3)$ 33 $c(c - 7)$
34 $p(4 - q)$ 35 $r(7 - s)$ 36 $a(8 - a)$
37 $b(5 - b)$ 38 $2x(y + z)$ 39 $3p(q + r)$
40 $6d(e + f)$ 41 $5a(b - c)$ 42 $4t(u - v)$
43 $3b(b + c)$ 44 $6m(m + n)$ 45 $4r(r - s)$
46 $7x(x - y)$ 47 $4c(d - c)$ 48 $6y(z - y)$
49 $3a(b + 4)$ 50 $2x(y + 5)$ 51 $4p(p + 2)$

If $3b + 4b = 7b$

then $3(b + 1) + 4(b + 1) = 7(b + 1)$

So $a(b + 1) + 4(b + 1) = (a + 4)(b + 1)$

$\therefore$ $(a + 4)(b + 1) = a(b + 1) + 4(b + 1)$

Example 7

Remove the brackets and simplify the following.

a $(a+2)(b+3)$ **b** $(a-2)(b-3)$
c $(a+2)(b-3)$ **d** $(a-2)(b+3)$

a $(a+2)(b+3) = a(b+3) + 2(b+3)$
$$= ab + 3a + 2b + 6$$

b $(a-2)(b-3) = a(b-3) - 2(b-3)$
$$= ab - 3a - 2b + 6$$

c $(a+2)(b-3) = a(b-3) + 2(b-3)$
$$= ab - 3a + 2b - 6$$

d $(a-2)(b+3) = a(b+3) - 2(b+3)$
$$= ab + 3a - 2b - 6$$

Example 8

Expand the following.

a $(x+3)(x+2)$ **b** $(x-4)(x-1)$
c $(a+3)(a-4)$ **d** $(p-5)(p+6)$

a $(x+3)(x+2) = x(x+2) + 3(x+2)$
$$= x^2 + \underline{2x + 3x} + 6$$
$$= x^2 + 5x + 6$$

b $(x-4)(x-1) = x(x-1) - 4(x-1)$
$$= x^2 \underline{- x - 4x} + 4$$
$$= x^2 - 5x + 4$$

c $(a+3)(a-4) = a(a-4) + 3(a-4)$
$$= a^2 \underline{- 4a + 3a} - 12$$
$$= a^2 - a - 12$$

d $(p-5)(p+6) = p(p+6) - 5(p+6)$
$$= p^2 + \underline{6p - 5p} - 30$$
$$= p^2 + p - 30$$

Exercise 2.8

Remove the brackets and simplify the following.

1 $(a+3)(b+4)$	**2** $(m+2)(n+5)$
3 $(c+4)(d+6)$	**4** $(u+1)(v+3)$
5 $(b+2)(c+2)$	**6** $(p+4)(q+2)$
7 $(x+6)(y+3)$	**8** $(e+5)(f+4)$
9 $(r+5)(s+1)$	**10** $(y+1)(z+1)$
11 $(x-2)(y-4)$	**12** $(p-3)(q-5)$
13 $(u-5)(v-6)$	**14** $(a-1)(b-4)$
15 $(m-3)(n-3)$	**16** $(r-5)(s-5)$
17 $(y-4)(z-3)$	**18** $(c-6)(d-2)$
19 $(u-5)(v-3)$	**20** $(x-3)(y-1)$
21 $(p+3)(q-5)$	**22** $(x+2)(y-6)$
23 $(a+4)(b-7)$	**24** $(m+1)(n-2)$
25 $(y+4)(z-4)$	**26** $(r+10)(s-10)$
27 $(b+6)(c-4)$	**28** $(m+8)(n-2)$
29 $(x+7)(y-3)$	**30** $(a+6)(b-1)$
31 $(m-2)(n+4)$	**32** $(x-3)(y+8)$
33 $(c-2)(d+7)$	**34** $(p-1)(q+5)$
35 $(a-6)(b+6)$	**36** $(y-2)(z+9)$

When the brackets have been removed, it is sometimes possible to collect like terms into a single term, for example:

$$(x+3)(x+4) = x(x+4) + 3(x+4)$$
$$= x^2 + \underline{4x + 3x} + 12$$
$$= x^2 + 7x + 12$$

Exercise 2.9

Expand the following.

1 $(x+4)(x+3)$	**2** $(y+5)(y+4)$
3 $(z+6)(z+2)$	**4** $(t+9)(t+5)$
5 $(a+3)(a+1)$	**6** $(b+7)(b+1)$
7 $(p+3)(p+5)$	**8** $(q+2)(q+8)$
9 $(r+4)(r+6)$	**10** $(s+5)(s+10)$
11 $(t+1)(t+5)$	**12** $(u+1)(u+9)$
13 $(a-5)(a-2)$	**14** $(b-6)(b-3)$
15 $(c-8)(c-4)$	**16** $(d-12)(d-5)$
17 $(e-4)(e-1)$	**18** $(f-10)(f-1)$
19 $(x-2)(x-4)$	**20** $(y-3)(y-7)$
21 $(z-5)(z-6)$	**22** $(t-6)(t-8)$
23 $(u-1)(u-2)$	**24** $(v-1)(v-6)$
25 $(a+5)(a-3)$	**26** $(b+7)(b-3)$
27 $(c+4)(c-2)$	**28** $(d+8)(d-5)$
29 $(x+3)(x-2)$	**30** $(y+5)(y-1)$
31 $(z+2)(z-1)$	**32** $(m+2)(m-6)$
33 $(n+3)(n-5)$	**34** $(p+4)(p-8)$
35 $(q+8)(q-10)$	**36** $(r+3)(r-4)$
37 $(s+1)(s-3)$	**38** $(x-5)(x+2)$
39 $(y-8)(y+3)$	**40** $(z-9)(z+2)$
41 $(t-7)(t+4)$	**42** $(a-5)(a+4)$

Example 9

Expand the following.

a $(a+3)^2$ b $(y-3)^2$ c $(x+3)(x-3)$

a $(a+3)^2 = (a+3)(a+3)$

$\quad\quad = a(a+3) = 3(a+3)$

$\quad\quad = a^2 + \underline{3a+3a} + 9$

$\quad\quad = a^2 + 6a + 9$

b $(y-3)^2 = (y-3)(y-3)$

$\quad\quad = y(y-3) - 3(y-3)$

$\quad\quad = y^2 - \underline{3y-3y} + 9$

$\quad\quad = y^2 - 6y + 9$

c $(x+3)(x-3) = x(x-3) = 3(x-3)$

$\quad\quad = x^2 - \underline{3x+3x} - 9$

$\quad\quad = x^2 - 9$

Exercise 2.10

Expand the following.

1 $(a+4)^2$	2 $(b+6)^2$	3 $(c+7)^2$
4 $(x+12)^2$	5 $(y+20)^2$	6 $(p-2)^2$
7 $(q-8)^2$	8 $(r-10)^2$	9 $(m-30)^2$
10 $(n-40)^2$	11 $(t+5)(t-5)$	
12 $(u+9)(u-9)$	13 $(v+1)(v-1)$	
14 $(d+11)(d-11)$	15 $(e+50)(e-50)$	

Factorizing

The value of 16×99 can be found as follows.

Because $\quad 99 = (100-1)$
then $\quad (16 \times 99) = 16 \times (100-1)$
$\quad\quad\quad = (16 \times 100) - (16 \times 1)$
$\quad\quad\quad = 1600 - 16$
$\quad\quad\quad = 1584$

In the same way,

$72 \times 102 = 72 \times (100+2)$
$\quad\quad\quad = (72 \times 100) + (72 \times 2)$
$\quad\quad\quad = 7200 + 144$
$\quad\quad\quad = 7344$

Exercise 2.11

Factorize to find the value of the following.

1 35×101	2 87×101	3 164×101
4 41×102	5 19×102	6 55×102
7 13×103	8 24×103	9 71×103
10 25×99	11 36×99	12 54×99
13 32×98	14 24×98	15 51×98
16 75×98	17 15×97	18 21×97
19 33×97	20 61×97	

Sometimes the reverse of the above method can be used to simplify calculations.

$(17 \times 84) + (17 \times 16) = 17 \times (84+16)$
$\quad\quad\quad\quad = 17 \times 100$
$\quad\quad\quad\quad = 1700$

Example 10

Find the value of the following.

a $(27 \times 16) - (27 \times 6)$

b $(7\frac{1}{2} \times 3\frac{1}{2}) + (7\frac{1}{2} \times 6\frac{1}{2})$

c $(1.2 \times 8.4) + (1.2 \times 1.6)$

a $(27 \times 16) - (27 \times 6) = 27 \times (16-6)$
$\quad\quad\quad\quad = 27 \times 10$
$\quad\quad\quad\quad = 270$

b $(7\frac{1}{2} \times 3\frac{1}{2}) + (7\frac{1}{2} \times 6\frac{1}{2}) = 7\frac{1}{2} \times (3\frac{1}{2} + 6\frac{1}{2})$
$\quad\quad\quad\quad = 7\frac{1}{2} \times 10$
$\quad\quad\quad\quad = 75$

c $(1.2 \times 8.4) + (1.2 \times 1.6) = 1.2 \times (8.4+1.6)$
$\quad\quad\quad\quad = 1.2 \times 10$
$\quad\quad\quad\quad = 12$

Exercise 2.12

Find the value of the following.

1 $(48 \times 19) - (48 \times 9)$
2 $(53 \times 28) - (53 \times 18)$
3 $(72 \times 57) - (72 \times 47)$
4 $(37 \times 96) - (37 \times 86)$
5 $(29 \times 81) - (29 \times 71)$
6 $(57 \times 64) + (57 \times 36)$
7 $(94 \times 73) + (94 \times 27)$
8 $(39 \times 55) + (39 \times 45)$
9 $(76 \times 92) + (76 \times 8)$
10 $(48 \times 87) + (48 \times 13)$

11 $(92 \times 160) - (92 \times 60)$
12 $(71 \times 540) - (71 \times 440)$
13 $(87 \times 960) - (87 \times 860)$
14 $(45 \times 490) - (45 \times 390)$
15 $(27 \times 730) - (27 \times 630)$
16 $(53 \times 680) + (53 \times 320)$
17 $(75 \times 810) + (75 \times 190)$
18 $(62 \times 740) + (62 \times 260)$
19 $(84 \times 530) + (84 \times 470)$
20 $(26 \times 940) + (26 \times 60)$
21 $(5 \times 7\frac{1}{2}) + (5 \times 2\frac{1}{2})$
22 $(8 \times 5\frac{1}{2}) + (8 \times 4\frac{1}{2})$
23 $(12 \times 9\frac{1}{2}) + (12 \times \frac{1}{2})$
24 $(2\frac{1}{2} \times 8\frac{1}{2}) + (2\frac{1}{2} \times 1\frac{1}{2})$
25 $(9 \times 96\frac{1}{2}) + (9 \times 3\frac{1}{2})$
26 $(7 \times 98\frac{1}{2}) + (7 \times 1\frac{1}{2})$
27 $(4 \times 6\frac{3}{4}) + (4 \times 3\frac{1}{4})$
28 $(11 \times 8\frac{3}{4}) + (11 \times 1\frac{1}{4})$
29 $(6 \times 9\frac{3}{4}) + (6 \times \frac{1}{4})$
30 $(1\frac{1}{2} \times 7\frac{3}{4}) + (1\frac{1}{2} \times 2\frac{1}{4})$
31 $(3\frac{1}{2} \times 5\frac{3}{4}) + (3\frac{1}{2} \times 4\frac{1}{4})$
32 $(3 \times 92\frac{3}{4}) + (3 \times 7\frac{1}{4})$
33 $(8 \times 94\frac{3}{4}) + (8 \times 5\frac{1}{4})$
34 $(9 \times 4\frac{2}{3}) + (9 \times 5\frac{1}{3})$
35 $(12 \times 3\frac{2}{3}) + (12 \times 6\frac{1}{3})$
36 $(7 \times \frac{2}{3}) + (7 \times 9\frac{1}{3})$
37 $(4\frac{1}{2} \times 2\frac{2}{3}) + (4\frac{1}{2} \times 7\frac{1}{3})$
38 $(7\frac{1}{2} \times 1\frac{2}{3}) + (7\frac{1}{2} \times 8\frac{1}{3})$
39 $(6 \times 97\frac{2}{3}) + (6 \times 2\frac{1}{3})$
40 $(11 \times 90\frac{2}{3}) + (11 \times 9\frac{1}{3})$
41 $(1.6 \times 7.5) + (1.6 \times 2.5)$
42 $(2.5 \times 6.7) + (2.5 \times 3.3)$
43 $(5.2 \times 5.6) + (5.2 \times 4.4)$
44 $(21 \times 8.8) + (21 \times 1.2)$
45 $(36 \times 9.4) + (36 \times 0.6)$
46 $(54 \times 7.75) + (54 \times 2.25)$
47 $(24.3 \times 6.15) + (24.3 \times 3.85)$
48 $(75.6 \times 5.65) + (75.6 \times 4.35)$
49 $(3.15 \times 8.95) + (3.15 \times 1.05)$
50 $(6.48 \times 9.45) + (6.48 \times 0.55)$
51 $(1.26 \times 67.5) + (1.26 \times 32.5)$
52 $(5.49 \times 51.5) + (5.49 \times 48.5)$
53 $(8.01 \times 75.5) + (8.01 \times 24.5)$
54 $(0.54 \times 80.5) + (0.54 \times 19.5)$
55 $(45 \times 96.5) + (45 \times 3.5)$
56 $(32 \times 82.4) + (32 \times 17.6)$
57 $(7 \times 65.2) + (7 \times 34.8)$
58 $(8.6 \times 71.9) + (8.6 \times 28.1)$
59 $(9.3 \times 53.7) + (9.3 \times 46.3)$
60 $(0.8 \times 68.75) + (0.8 \times 31.25)$

A similar method can be used to simplify expressions such as $2x + 2y$.

$$2x + 2y = (2 \times x) + (2 \times y)$$
$$= 2 \times (x + y)$$
$$= 2(x + y)$$

This process of taking out a common factor is known as *factorizing*. Here the common factor is 2.

Example 12

Factorize the following.

a $4x - 4y$ **b** $3x^2 + 3y^2$ **c** $ax + ay$

$$\begin{aligned} \textbf{a} \quad 4x - 4y &= (4 \times x) - (4 \times y) \\ &= 4 \times (x - y) \\ &= 4(x - y) \end{aligned}$$

$$\begin{aligned} \textbf{b} \quad 3x^2 + 3y^2 &= (3 \times x^2) + (3 \times y^2) \\ &= 3 \times (x^2 + y^2) \\ &= 3(x^2 + y^2) \end{aligned}$$

$$\begin{aligned} \textbf{c} \quad ax + ay &= (a \times x) + (a \times y) \\ &= a \times (x + y) \\ &= a(x + y) \end{aligned}$$

Exercise 2.13

Factorize the following.

1 $4x + 4y$	**2** $3u + 3v$	**3** $6a + 6b$
4 $9m + 9n$	**5** $7p + 7q$	**6** $2a^2 + 2b^2$
7 $5x^2 + 5y^2$	**8** $8u^2 + 8v^2$	**9** $10m^2 + 10n^2$
10 $6p - 6q$	**11** $3a - 3b$	**12** $9x - 9y$
13 $7m - 7n$	**14** $5u^2 - 5v^2$	**15** $8x^2 - 8y^2$
16 $9a^2 - 9b^2$	**17** $3p^2 - 3q^2$	**18** $am + an$
19 $bu + bv$	**20** $cx + cy$	**21** $dp + dq$
22 $mu^2 + mv^2$	**23** $nr^2 + ns^2$	**24** $px^2 + py^2$
25 $qa^2 + qb^2$	**26** $mx - my$	**27** $nu - nv$
28 $pa - pb$	**29** $qc - qd$	**30** $ar^2 - as^2$
31 $bp^2 - bq^2$	**32** $cx^2 - cy^2$	**33** $dm^2 - dn^2$
34 $x^2 + xy$	**35** $p^2 + pq$	**36** $u^2 + uv$
37 $a^2 + ab$	**38** $r^2 + rs$	**39** $c^2 - cd$
40 $y^2 - yz$	**41** $m^2 - mn$	**42** $t^2 - tu$
43 $bc + c^2$	**44** $de + e^2$	**45** $yz + z^2$
46 $np + p^2$	**47** $kl + l^2$	**48** $qr - r^2$
49 $ef - f^2$	**50** $st - t^2$	**51** $lm - m^2$
52 $cd - d^2$	**53** $ax^2 + bx^2$	**54** $cy^2 + dy^2$
55 $mt^2 + nt^2$	**56** $pz^2 + qz^2$	**57** $ku^2 - lu^2$
58 $qv^2 - rv^2$	**59** $br^2 - cr^2$	**60** $ds^2 - es^2$

With practice, this type of factorizing can be done on sight.

Example 13

Factorize the following.

a $5a + 5b$ **b** $7x - 14y$ **c** $6a - 8b$

a $5a + 5b = 5(a + b)$

b $7x - 14y = 7(x - 2y)$

c $6a - 8b = 2(3a - 4b)$

Exercise 2.14

Factorize the following.

1 $2a + 2b$	**2** $8c + 8d$
3 $3m + 2n$	**4** $9x - 9y$
5 $5u - 5v$	**6** $12p - 12q$
7 $2a + 6b$	**8** $2c + 10d$
9 $3m + 12n$	**10** $3p + 21q$
11 $5u + 10v$	**12** $5x + 25y$
13 $3b - 15c$	**14** $3d - 24e$
15 $4r - 12s$	**16** $4y - 20z$
17 $6m - 18n$	**18** $6t - 30u$
19 $8x + 2y$	**20** $12u + 2v$
21 $18p + 3q$	**22** $30m + 3n$
23 $24a + 6b$	**24** $36c + 6d$
25 $8m - 4n$	**26** $16p - 4q$
27 $15r - 5s$	**28** $40x - 5y$
29 $21u - 7v$	**30** $35k - 7l$
31 $4a + 6b$	**32** $8c + 10d$
33 $6m + 9n$	**34** $9p + 21q$
35 $10r + 15s$	**36** $6u - 10v$
37 $10x - 14y$	**38** $9b - 15c$
39 $10d - 25e$	**40** $20k - 35l$
41 $14x + 8y$	**42** $16u + 10v$

$$15^2 - 5^2$$

The above expression is called the *difference between two squares*. It can be simplified as follows.

$$15^2 - 5^2 = (15 + 5) \times (15 - 5)$$
$$= 20 \times 10$$
$$= 200$$

Example 14

Find the value of the following.

a $6^2 - 4^2$ **b** $75^2 - 25^2$
c $99^2 - 1^2$ **d** $6.8^2 - 3.2^2$
e $(7\frac{1}{2})^2 - (2\frac{1}{2})^2$

a $6^2 - 4^2 = (6 + 4) \times (6 - 4)$
$$= 10 \times 2 = 20$$

b $75^2 - 25^2 = (75 + 25) \times (75 - 25)$
$$= 100 \times 50 = 5000$$

c $99^2 - 1^2 = (99 + 1) \times (99 - 1)$
$$= 100 \times 98 = 9800$$

d $6.8^2 - 3.2^2 = (6.8 + 3.2) \times (6.8 - 3.2)$
$$= 10 \times 3.6 = 36$$

e $(7\frac{1}{2})^2 - (2\frac{1}{2})^2 = (7\frac{1}{2} + 2\frac{1}{2}) \times (7\frac{1}{2} - 2\frac{1}{2})$
$$= 10 \times 5 = 50$$

Exercise 2.15

Find the value of the following.

1 $7^2 - 3^2$	**2** $8^2 - 2^2$
3 $9^2 - 1^2$	**4** $11^2 - 1^2$
5 $12^2 - 2^2$	**6** $16^2 - 6^2$
7 $18^2 - 8^2$	**8** $19^2 - 9^2$
9 $60^2 - 40^2$	**10** $70^2 - 30^2$
11 $90^2 - 10^2$	**12** $80^2 - 20^2$
13 $85^2 - 15^2$	**14** $65^2 - 35^2$
15 $55^2 - 45^2$	**16** $68^2 - 32^2$
17 $77^2 - 23^2$	**18** $56^2 - 44^2$
19 $89^2 - 11^2$	**20** $82^2 - 18^2$
21 $64^2 - 36^2$	**22** $125^2 - 25^2$
23 $132^2 - 32^2$	**24** $155^2 - 55^2$
25 $95^2 - 5^2$	**26** $98^2 - 2^2$
27 $96^2 - 4^2$	**28** $97^2 - 3^2$
29 $92^2 - 8^2$	**30** $93^2 - 7^2$
31 $94^2 - 6^2$	**32** $91^2 - 9^2$
33 $101^2 - 1^2$	**34** $102^2 - 2^2$
35 $105^2 - 5^2$	**36** $108^2 - 8^2$
37 $7.9^2 - 2.1^2$	**38** $8.6^2 - 1.4^2$
39 $6.7^2 - 3.3^2$	**40** $5.8^2 - 4.2^2$
41 $8.5^2 - 1.5^2$	**42** $9.5^2 - 0.5^2$
43 $9.7^2 - 0.3^2$	**44** $7.3^2 - 2.7^2$
45 $6.4^2 - 3.6^2$	**46** $8.2^2 - 1.8^2$
47 $5.1^2 - 4.9^2$	**48** $9.4^2 - 0.6^2$
49 $(8\frac{1}{2})^2 - (1\frac{1}{2})^2$	**50** $(6\frac{1}{2})^2 - (3\frac{1}{2})^2$
51 $(5\frac{1}{2})^2 - (4\frac{1}{2})^2$	**52** $(9\frac{1}{2})^2 - \frac{1}{2}^2$
53 $(7\frac{3}{4})^2 - (2\frac{1}{4})^2$	**54** $(8\frac{3}{4})^2 - (1\frac{1}{4})^2$

$x^2 - 9$ is equal to $x^2 - 3^2$

So the expression $x^2 - 9$ is another example of the 'difference between two squares'.

$$x^2 - 9 = x^2 - 3^2 = (x + 3) \times (x - 3)$$
$$= (x + 3)(x - 3)$$

The expressions $(x + 3)$ and $(x - 3)$ are called the *factors* of $x^2 - 9$.

Example 15

Factorize the following.

a $a^2 - 25$ **b** $49 - y^2$ **c** $p^2 - 1$

a $a^2 - 25 = a^2 - 5^2 = (a + 5) \times (a - 5)$
                        $= (a + 5)(a - 5)$

b $49 - y^2 = 7^2 - y^2 = (7 + y) \times (7 - y)$
                       $= (7 + y)(7 - y)$

c $p^2 - 1 = p^2 - 1^2 = (p + 1) \times (p - 1)$
                     $= (p + 1)(p - 1)$

Exercise 2.16

Factorize the following.

1 $x^2 - 16$	2 $y^2 - 49$	3 $z^2 - 81$
4 $p^2 - 64$	5 $q^2 - 36$	6 $r^2 - 4$
7 $a^2 - 100$	8 $b^2 - 144$	9 $c^2 - 121$
10 $m^2 - 400$	11 $n^2 - 900$	12 $u^2 - 2500$
13 $v^2 - 1600$	14 $x^2 - 3600$	15 $y^2 - 225$
16 $z^2 - 625$	17 $a^2 - \frac{1}{4}$	18 $b^2 - \frac{1}{9}$
19 $c^2 - \frac{1}{25}$	20 $m^2 - \frac{1}{16}$	21 $n^2 - \frac{1}{100}$
22 $u^2 - \frac{1}{36}$	23 $v^2 - \frac{1}{64}$	24 $r^2 - \frac{1}{81}$
25 $s^2 - \frac{1}{49}$	26 $9 - a^2$	27 $25 - b^2$
28 $16 - c^2$	29 $4 - d^2$	30 $64 - m^2$
31 $36 - n^2$	32 $81 - p^2$	33 $1 - q^2$
34 $100 - r^2$	35 $144 - s^2$	36 $121 - t^2$
37 $900 - x^2$	38 $400 - y^2$	39 $1600 - z^2$
40 $2500 - a^2$	41 $6400 - b^2$	42 $4900 - c^2$
43 $225 - d^2$	44 $\frac{1}{25} - u^2$	45 $\frac{1}{100} - v^2$
46 $\frac{1}{9} - m^2$	47 $\frac{1}{16} - n^2$	48 $\frac{1}{4} - x^2$
49 $\frac{1}{36} - y^2$	50 $\frac{1}{144} - z^2$	

Solving equations

Reminder
Both sides of an equation must be equal.
If one side of the equation is changed, then the other side must be changed in *exactly* the same way.

Example 16

Solve $3x + 8 + 2x = 23$

	$3x + 8 + 2x = 23$
Collect like terms	$5x + 8 = 23$
Take 8 from both sides	$5x = 15$
Divide both sides by 5	$x = 3$

Exercise 2.17

Solve the following.

1 $4x + 5 + 3x = 26$	2 $7x + 3 + 2x = 21$
3 $6y + 12 + 5y = 56$	4 $5y + 7 + y = 31$
5 $z + 9 + 7z = 25$	6 $3a - 6 + 2a = 9$
7 $5b - 8 + 4b = 28$	8 $4c - 12 + 2c = 18$
9 $9d - 16 + 3d = 20$	10 $6e - 30 + e = 12$
11 $8p + 11 - 3p = 31$	12 $9q + 12 - 2q = 40$
13 $12r + 14 - 6r = 50$	14 $11s + 6 - 3s = 30$
15 $12t + 16 - t = 60$	16 $7x - 8 - 2x = 17$
17 $8y - 9 - 4y = 23$	18 $12z - 6 - 5z = 15$
19 $15u - 13 - 9u = 29$	20 $20v - 14 - 12v = 18$

Sometimes, letters and numbers appear on both sides of an equation.

e.g. $4x + 5 = 14 + x$

In such cases, collect all the letters on one side of the equation, and all the numbers on the other side.
Make sure that both sides are changed in the same way so that the equation is still balanced.

Example 17

Solve $3a = 8 - a$

	$3a = 8 - a$
Add a to both sides	$3a + a = 8 - a + a$
Collect like terms	$4a = 8$
Divide both sides by 4	$a = 2$

Example 18

Solve $3x + 5 = 2x$

$$3x + 5 = 2x$$

Take $2x$ from both sides $3x - 2x + 5 = 2x - 2x$
Collect like terms $x + 5 = 0$
Take 5 from both sides $x = -5$

Exercise 2.18

Solve the following.

1   $3x = 15 - 2x$ 2 $5x = 16 - 3x$
3   $4y = 36 - 5y$ 4 $6z = 35 - z$
5   $3t = 4 - t$ 6 $5a = 8 + 3a$
7   $8b = 18 + 5b$ 8 $9c = 15 + 4c$
9   $6d = 2 + 5d$ 10 $7e = 30 + e$
11   $9m = 7m + 10$ 12 $6n = 2n + 28$
13   $12p = 10p + 4$ 14 $9q = 8q + 6$
15   $5r = r + 32$ 16 $6x = 2x - 8$
17   $7y = 3y - 16$ 18 $8z = 4z - 12$
19   $3u = 2u - 5$ 20 $4v = v - 18$
21   $6p - 8 = 2p$ 22 $9q - 25 = 4q$
23   $13r - 12 = 10r$ 24 $2s - 7 = s$
25   $10t - 9 = t$ 26 $9a + 12 = 5a$
27   $7b + 10 = 2b$ 28 $8c + 30 = 3c$
29   $4m + 15 = m$ 30 $7n + 12 = 6n$

Example 19

Solve $3a + 5 = a + 9$

$$3a + 5 = a + 9$$

Take a from both sides $2a + 5 = 9$
Take 5 from both sides $2a = 4$
Divide both sides by 2 $a = 2$

Example 20

Solve $2b - 4 = 8 - b$

$$2b - 4 = 8 - b$$

Add b to both sides $3b - 4 = 8$
Add 4 to both sides $3b = 12$
Divide both sides by 3 $b = 4$

Exercise 2.19

Solve the following.

1   $6a + 2 = 2a + 10$ 2 $9b + 3 = 6b + 18$
3   $12c + 9 = 7c + 14$ 4 $11d + 9 = 4d + 30$
5   $5e + 8 = 4e + 15$ 6 $7f + 8 = f + 20$
7   $8p - 7 = 6p + 3$ 8 $9q - 8 = 3q + 16$
9   $11r - 12 = 8r + 6$ 10 $20s - 3 = 11s + 6$
11   $15t - 2 = 14t + 5$ 12 $5u - 12 = u + 20$
13   $5x - 9 = 2x - 3$ 14 $7y - 10 = 5y - 2$
15   $9z - 14 = 6z - 5$ 16 $15t - 56 = 7t - 16$
17   $10u - 20 = 9u - 11$ 18 $9v - 40 = v - 24$
19   $4m - 5 = 7 - 2m$ 20 $5n - 8 = 32 - 3n$

Sometimes brackets have to be removed before the equation can be solved.

Example 21

Solve $3(x + 2) = 18 - x$

$$3(x + 2) = 18 - x$$

Remove the brackets $3x + 6 = 18 - x$
Add x to both sides, then subtract 6 from both sides $3x + x = 18 - 6$
Collect like terms $4x = 12$
Divide both sides by 4 $x = 3$

Example 22

Solve $4(a - 2) = 2(a + 5)$

$$4(a - 2) = 2(a + 5)$$

Remove the brackets $4a - 8 = 2a + 10$
Add 8 to both sides, then subtract $2a$ from both sides $4a - 2a = 10 + 8$
Collect like terms $2a = 18$
Divide both sides by 2 $a = 9$

Exercise 2.20

1   $5(x + 2) = 2x + 16$ 2 $7(x + 3) = 5x + 29$
3   $4(y + 1) = y + 13$ 4 $8(z - 2) = 3z + 9$
5   $6(t - 3) = 2t + 10$ 6 $9(u - 1) = 8u + 3$
7   $5(v - 4) = 2v - 5$ 8 $7(m - 2) = 5m - 4$
9   $4(n - 5) = n - 2$ 10 $3(a - 2) = 9 - 2a$
11   $4(b - 5) = 8 - 3b$ 12 $6(c - 3) = 4 - 5c$
13   $2(p + 3) = 21 - 3p$ 14 $5(q + 1) = 12 - 2q$
15   $4(r + 2) = 33 - r$ 16 $8(x + 2) = 3(x + 7)$
17   $7(y + 2) = 2(y + 12)$ 18 $9(z + 1) = 5(z + 5)$
19   $5(t - 2) = 2(t + 4)$ 20 $7(u - 3) = 3(u + 5)$

Example 23

Solve $5(x + 2) + 2(x - 1) = 22$

$$5(x + 2) + 2(x - 1) = 22$$

Remove the brackets $5x + 10 + 2x - 2 = 22$

Collect like terms $7x + 8 = 22$

Subtract 8 from both sides $7x = 14$

Divide both sides by 7 $x = 2$

Example 24

Solve $4(a - 2) - 2(a - 3) = 6$

$$4(a - 2) - 2(a - 3) = 6$$

Remove the brackets $4a - 8 - 2a + 6 = 6$

Collect like terms $2a - 2 = 6$

Add 2 to both sides $2a = 8$

Divide both sides by 2 $a = 4$

Exercise 2.21

Solve the following.

1 $3(x + 2) + 2(x + 1) = 23$
2 $4(x + 3) + 3(x + 2) = 32$
3 $5(y + 1) + 3(y + 4) = 25$
4 $3(z + 4) + 2(z - 3) = 26$
5 $5(t + 2) + 3(t - 1) = 31$
6 $4(a + 1) = 3(a - 4) = 13$
7 $2(b + 1) + 4(b - 3) = 20$
8 $2(m - 3) + 3(m + 4) = 16$
9 $3(n - 1) + 4(n + 2) = 12$
10 $4(p - 3) + 2(p + 4) = 14$
11 $5(q - 2) + 3(q + 1) = 33$
12 $3(x - 2) + 2(x - 4) = 6$
13 $4(y - 1) + 3(y - 5) = 2$
14 $5(z - 2) + 3(z - 4) = 10$
15 $5(a + 2) - 2(a + 3) = 19$
16 $8(b + 3) - 4(b + 4) = 12$
17 $4(c + 2) - 2(c + 5) = 14$
18 $6(d + 1) - 3(d + 4) = 21$
19 $5(t - 1) - 3(t + 2) = 1$
20 $6(u - 2) - 2(u + 4) = 8$

Unit 3   Probability

Mutually exclusive events

If events are *mutually exclusive* this means that if one happens the other(s) cannot happen and vice versa. In such cases, the probabilities of the events happening must add to one.

Example 1

The probability that it rains tomorrow is 0.3. What is the probability that it does not rain tomorrow?

Raining and not raining are mutually exclusive events so the probability that it does not rain is

$$1 - 0.3 = 0.7$$

Example 2

There are three kinds of sweet in a bag, mints, toffees and lime creams. If a sweet is picked at random, the probability that it is a mint is 0.37 and the probability that it is a toffee is 0.51. What is the probability that it is a lime cream?

Selecting the three different sweets are mutually exclusive events so the probability that the sweet is a lime cream is

$$1 - (0.37 + 0.51) = 1 - 0.88 = 0.12$$

Exercise 3.1

1   The probability that Peter is late for school is 0.06.
    What is the probability that Peter is not late for school?
2   The probability that a weekday selected at random is a Wednesday is 0.2.
    What is the probability that a weekday selected at random is not a Wednesday?
3   The probability that a light bulb fails in the first 1000 hours of use is 0.15.
    What is the probability that it does not fail in the first 1000 hours of use?
4   A bag contains red and white beads. The probability that a bead selected at random is red is 0.67.
    What is the probability that a bead selected at random is white?

5   A bag contains red and white beads. The probability that a bead selected at random is white is 0.25.
    a   What is the probability that a bead selected at random is red?
    b   If there are 4 beads in the bag, how many are red?
    c   If there are 28 beads in the bag, how many are white?
    d   Explain why there cannot be 10 beads in the bag.

6   A bag contains red and white beads. The probability that a bead selected at random is white is 0.375.
    a   What is the probability that a bead selected at random is red?
    b   If there are 8 beads in the bag, how many are red?
    c   If there are 64 beads in the bag, how many are white?
    d   Explain why there cannot be 28 beads in the bag.

7   A bag contains red, white and blue beads. The probability that a bead selected at random is red is 0.1 and the probability that a bead selected at random is white is 0.3.
    a   What is the probability that a bead selected at random is blue?
    b   If there are 10 beads in the bag, how many are red?
    c   If there are 80 beads in the bag, how many are blue?
    d   Explain why there cannot be 12 beads in the bag.

8   A bag contains red, white and blue beads. The probability that a bead selected at random is red is 0.125 and the probability that a bead selected at random is white is 0.2.
    a   What is the probability that a bead selected at random is blue?
    b   If there are 40 beads in the bag, how many are red?
    c   If there are 120 beads in the bag, how many are blue?
    d   Explain why there cannot be 12 beads in the bag.

9 The probability that it rains on a June day in Gedney is 0.13.
  a What is the probability that it does not rain on a June day in Gedney?
  b On how many days in Gedney would you predict it will rain next June?
  c On how many days in Gedney would you predict it will not rain next June?

10 In a restaurant, all means are offered with either chips or baked potatoes. The probability that a person chooses chips with their meal is 0.75.
  a What is the probability that a person chooses baked potato with their meal?
  b If the restaurant serves 120 meals in one day, estimate how many are served with chips.
  c If the restaurant serves 2260 meals in one month, estimate how many are served with baked potato.

11 The approximate probability of getting 6 numbers correct and winning the Jackpot in the National Lottery is 0.000 000 071. Mr Smith plays 5 lines each week.
  a What is the probability that Mr Smith wins the Jackpot in any given week?
  b What is the probability that Mr Smith does not win the Jackpot in any given week?

If events are not connected in any way they are independent.
For example, if we toss a coin and roll a dice the events are independent because the outcome of the coin is not connected in any way to the outcome of the dice.

If several events are independent or mutually exclusive we can find the probability that they will all happen by multiplying the individual probabilities.

Example 3

Find the probability of rolling four dice and obtaining 4 even numbers.

The probability of rolling one dice and obtaining an even number is $\frac{1}{2}$ or 0.5.

The probability of rolling four dice and getting four even numbers is therefore

$$0.5 \times 0.5 \times 0.5 \times 0.5 = 0.0625$$

Example 4

A bag contains 3 red and 5 white beads. Three beads are selected one after the other, each bead being returned to the bag before the other is selected.
Find the probability that they are all red.

probability first bead is red $= \frac{3}{8} = 0.375$

probability second bead is red $= \frac{3}{8} = 0.375$

probability third bead is red $= \frac{3}{8} = 0.375$

probability that all three beads are red

$$= 0.375 \times 0.375 \times 0.375 = 0.053 \text{ (to 3 dp)}$$

Exercise 3.2

1 Find the probability of tossing six coins and getting six heads.

2 Joe and Soraya walk to school together. The probability that Joe wears red socks is 0.3, the probability that Soraya wears yellow socks is 0.1 and the probability that it rains tomorrow is 0.12. What is the probability that tomorrow it rains, Joe wears red socks and Soraya wears yellow socks?

3 If you write to ask for a place in the audience of a certain quiz show your probability of getting a ticket is 0.25.
If you are in the audience your probability of being selected to take part in the quiz is 0.02.
If you are selected to take part in the quiz your probability of winning is 0.125.
What is the probability that somebody writing in for a ticket will eventually win the quiz?

4 A bag contains 3 red and 7 white beads. A bead is drawn from the bag, its colour is noted and then it is returned to the bag. This is done 3 times.

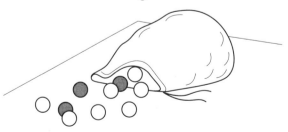

Find the probability that
  a all three beads are red
  b all three beads are white
  c a red bead is followed by two white beads.

5 A bag contains 2 red, 3 white and 5 blue beads. A bead is drawn from the bag, its colour is noted and then it is returned to the bag. This is done 3 times.
Find the probability that
a all three beads are red
b all three beads are blue
c a red bead is followed by a white bead and then a blue bead.

6 A normal pack of 52 cards is shuffled and cut. The selected card is noted and then returned to the pack. This is done 3 times.

Find the probability that
a all three cards are red
b all three cards are clubs
c all three cards are Aces.

7 There are 100 members in a monthly charity prize draw club, 45 of whom are men and 55 of whom are women. Every month each member pays £1 and a single name is selected at random to win the £50 monthly prize, the other £50 going to charity.
Find the probability that
a three prizes in a row are won by women
b three prizes in a row are won by me
c three prizes in a row are won by the same person.

8 There are 25 pupils in a class, 10 boys and 15 girls. Each lesson the teacher selects a pupil at random to give out books and equipment.

Find the probability that
a a girl is selected for four lessons in a row
b a boy is selected for four lessons in a row
c the same pupil is selected for four lessons in a row.

Example 5

Tom uses two machines at work. The probability that the first machine fails during a shift is 0.04 and the probability that the second machine fails is 0.1.
What is the probability that neither machine fails during a shift?

Probability that first machine does not fail is

$$1 - 0.04 = 0.96$$

Probability that second machine does not fail is

$$1 - 0.1 = 0.9$$

Probability that neither machine fails is

$$0.96 \times 0.9 = 0.864$$

Exercise 3.3

1 There are a number of red and white beads in a bag. The probability that a bead selected at random is red is 0.3.
Three beads are selected at random, each being returned to the bag before the next is selected.
Find the probability that
a all three beads are red
b all three beads are white
c a red bead is followed by two white beads.

2 If Kayleigh selects a pen at random from her pencil case, the probability that it is blue is 0.08. Kayleigh selects three pens at random, returning each to the pencil case before she selects another.

Find the probability that
a all three are blue
b none are blue
c two blue pens are followed by one which is not blue.

3 John and Ajay walk to school together.
   The probability that John wears white socks is
   0.2. The probability that Ajay wears white socks
   is 0.1.
   Find the probability that
   a both boys wear white socks
   b neither wears white socks
   c John wears white socks but Ajay does not wear
         white socks
   d Ajay wears white socks but John does not wear
         white socks.

4 Mr Brown travels to work by car and his route
   takes him through a set of traffic lights, over a
   railway crossing and past a farm.
   The probability that he is delayed by the lights is
   0.5.
   The probability that he is delayed by the railway
   crossing is 0.2 and the probability that he is
   delayed by farm animals on the road is 0.05.
   If he meets all three delays he is late for work.

   Find the probability that
   a Mr Brown is delayed by the lights and the
         crossing but not by farm animals
   b Mr Brown is delayed by farm animals and the
         lights but not by the crossing
   c Mr Brown is late for work
   d Mr Brown is not delayed by the lights, the
         crossing or the farm animals.

5 A bag contains a mixture of green, yellow and
   purple beads. If a bead is selected at random, the
   probability that it is green is 0.1 and the
   probability that it is yellow is 0.3.
   Three beads are selected at random from the bag,
   with each bead being replaced in the bag before
   the next is selected.
   Find the probability that
   a all three beads are yellow
   b all three beads are green
   c all three beads are purple
   d a yellow bead is followed by a green bead and
         then a purple bead.

Example 6

A bag contains 3 red and 5 white beads.
If three beads are selected one after the other
and not returned to the bag, find the probability
that they are all red.

probability first bead is red $= \frac{3}{8} = 0.375$

There are now 7 beads left, 2 of which are red
so,

probability second bead is red $= \frac{2}{7} = 0.286$

There are now 6 beads left, 1 of which is red so,

probability third bead is red $= \frac{1}{6} = 0.167$

probability that all three beads are red

$$= 0.375 \times 0.286 \times 0.167 = 0.018 \text{ (to 3 dp)}$$

Example 7

Three cards are dealt face up on a table from the
top of a normal pack.
Find the probability that all three cards are
Aces.

probability of first Ace $= \frac{4}{52} = 0.077$

probability of second Ace $= \frac{3}{51} = 0.059$

probability of third Ace $= \frac{2}{50} = 0.04$

probability of all three Aces

$$= 0.077 \times 0.059 \times 0.04 = 0.000\,18$$

Exercise 3.4

1 A bag contains 3 red and 7 white beads. A bead is
   drawn from the bag and not replaced.
   This is done 3 times.
   Find the probability that
   a all three beads are red
   b all three beads are white
   c a red bead is followed by two white beads.

2 A bag contains 2 red, 3 white and 5 blue beads. A
   bead is drawn from the bag and not replaced.
   This is done 3 times.
   Find the probability that
   a all three beads are white
   b all three beads are blue
   c a red bead is followed by a white bead and
         then a blue bead.

3 A normal pack of 52 cards is shuffled and cut. The selected card is not returned to the pack. This is done 3 times.
Find the probability that
a all three cards are red
b all three cards are clubs
c all three cards are Kings.

4 Jodie has 4 pens and 8 felt tips in her pencil case. She selects three items at random from the case and does not replace them.
Find the probability that
a all three are pens
b none are pens.

5 There are 20 televisions in a batch, of which three are faulty. A quality control inspector selects three televisions to test.

Find the probability that
a the first television selected is faulty
b the first television selected is working correctly but the second television selected is faulty
c the first and second televisions selected are working correctly but the third is faulty
d three televisions that all work correctly are selected
e all three faulty televisions are selected.

6 There are 25 eggs in a fridge, 4 of which are bad. Salina selects 3 eggs at random to make an omelet.

Find the probability that
a the first egg Salina selects is bad
b the first egg Salina selects is good
c the first two eggs Salina selects are good
d Salina selects three good eggs
e Salina selects three bad eggs.

Tree diagrams

Example 8

A bag contains 3 red and 5 white beads. Two beads are selected one after the other, each bead being returned to the bag before the other is selected. Find the probability that

a one bead is red   **b** at least one bead is red.

First, we draw a tree diagram.

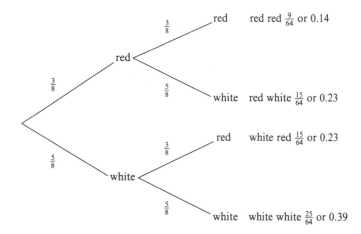

In this tree diagram we place a probability on each branch and *multiply* these probabilities to find the probability of each possible combination of colours.

a Two results contain one red bead so
probability of obtaining one red bead $= 0.23 + 0.23 = 0.46$
b Three results contain at least one red bead so
probability of obtaining at least one red bead $= 0.14 + 0.23 + 0.23 = 0.6$

Exercise 3.5

1 A bag contains 3 red and 7 white beads. Two beads are selected one after the other, each bead being returned to the bag before the other is selected.

a Copy and complete this tree diagram.

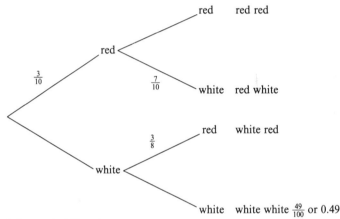

b Find the probability that
(i) one bead is white   (ii) at least one bead is white.

2 A bag contains 1 red and 3 white beads. Two beads are selected one after the other, each bead being returned to the bag before the other is selected.
a Copy and complete this tree diagram.

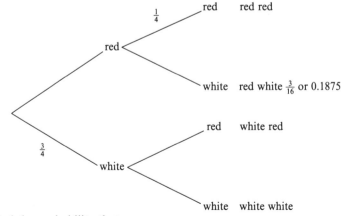

b Find the probability that
(i) one bead is white   (ii) at least one bead is white
(iii) neither bead is white   (iv) two beads of the same colour are selected.

3 A bag contains 2 red, 3 white and 5 blue beads. A bead is drawn from the bag, its colour noted and then it is returned to the bag.
This is repeated twice.
   a Copy and complete this tree diagram.

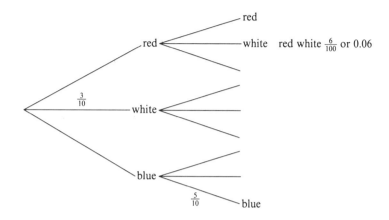

   b Find the probability that
      (i) both beads are red
      (ii) both beads are blue
      (iii) a red and a white bead are selected (in any order)
      (iv) one white bead is included in the selection
      (v) no red beads are included in the selection
      (vi) at least one blue bead is selected.

4 A normal pack of 52 cards is shuffled and cut. The selected card is noted and then returned to the pack.
This is repeated 2 times.
Draw a tree diagram and find the probability that
   a both cards are red
   b one card is red
   c at least one card is red
   d neither card is red.

5 There are 100 members in a monthly charity prize draw club, 45 of whom are men and 55 of whom are women. Every month each member pays £1 and a single name is selected at random to win the £50 monthly prize, the other £50 going to charity.
Draw a tree diagram and find the probability that
   a the June and July prizes are both won by women.
   b at least one of the June and July prizes is won by a woman.
   c the June and July prizes are won by one man and one woman (in either order).

6 There are 25 pupils in a class, 10 boys and 15 girls.
Each lesson the teacher selects a pupil at random to give out books and equipment.
Draw a tree diagram and find the probability that
a a girl is selected for two lessons in a row
b a boy is selected for two lessons in a row
c one boy and one girl are selected in two lessons in a row (in either order)
d at least one girl is selected in two lessons in a row.

7 In a restaurant, all meals are offered with either chips or baked potatoes. The probability that a person chooses chips with their meal is 0.75.
Draw a tree diagram and find the probability that when two people eat in the restaurant
a both choose chips
b both choose baked potatoes
c one chooses chips
d at least one chooses chips
e at least one chooses baked potato.

8 A bag contains red, white and blue beads. The probability that a bead selected at random is red is 0.1 and the probability that a bead selected at random is white is 0.5.
A bead is drawn from the bag, its colour is noted and then it is returned to the bag. This is repeated twice.
Draw a tree diagram and find the probability that
a both beads are red
b both beads are blue
c a red and a white bead are selected (in any order)
d one white bead is included in the selection
e no red beads are included in the selection
f at least one blue bead is selected.

Example 9

There are 25 eggs in a fridge, 4 of which are bad. Salina selects 2 eggs at random to make an omelet.
Find the probability that Salina selects at least 1 bad egg.

To answer this question we first construct a tree diagram.

Salina would not select an egg and then put it back in the fridge, so obviously this is selecting without replacement.

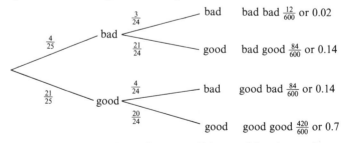

The diagram shows that of the four possible combinations of eggs, three contain at least one bad egg. The combined probability is therefore

$$0.02 + 0.14 + 0.14 = 0.3$$

Exercise 3.6

1 A bag contains 3 red and 7 white beads. Two are selected one after the other. The first is **not** returned to the bag before the second is selected.

   a Copy and complete this tree diagram.

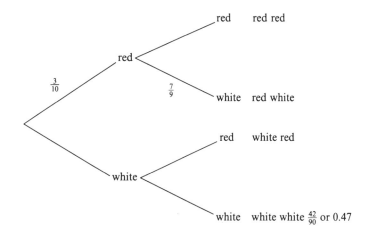

   b Find the probability that
   (i) one bead is white   (ii) at least one bead is white.

2 A bag contains 1 red and 3 white beads. Two beads are selected one after the other. The first is **not** returned to the bag before the second is selected.

   a Copy and complete this tree diagram.

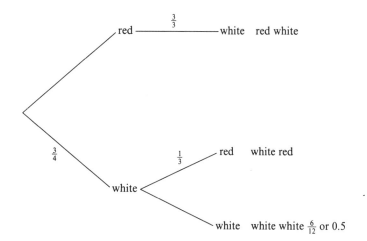

   b Find the probability that
   (i) one bead is white   (ii) at least one bead is white
   (iii) neither bead is white (iv) two beads of the same colour are selected.

3 A bag contains 2 red, 3 white and 5 blue beads. Two beads are selected one after the other. The first is **not** returned to the bag before the second is selected.

a Copy and complete this tree diagram.

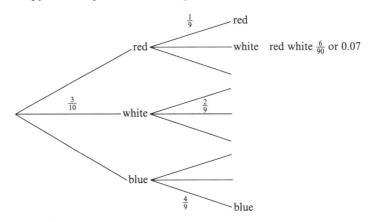

red white $\frac{6}{90}$ or 0.07

b Find the probability that
  (i) both beads are red
  (ii) both beads are blue
  (iii) a red and a white bead are selected (in any order)
  (iv) one white bead is included in the selection
  (v) no red beads are included in the selection
  (vi) at least one blue bead is selected.

4 A normal pack of 52 cards is shuffled and cut.
The selected card is **not** returned to the pack.
This is repeated.
Draw a tree diagram and find the probability that
a both cards are red
b at least one of the cards is red
c neither card is red.

5 Sally has 4 pens and 8 felt tips in her pencil case.
She selects two items at random from the case.
Draw a tree diagram and find the probability that
a both are pens
b at least one is a pen
c neither are pens.

6 There are 20 televisions in a batch, of which three are faulty. A quality control inspector selects three televisions to test.
Draw a tree diagram and find the probability that at least one of the selected sets is faulty.

7 One year, 5 of the 30 days in September are Mondays. A company quality inspector picks 3 days at random in that month to visit and check a fast food restaurant (which opens 7 days a week).
Draw a tree diagram and find the probability that
a the inspector selects at least 2 Mondays
b the inspector selects 3 days that are not Mondays
c the inspector selects at least 1 Monday.

8 One bag contains 2 red and 3 white beads.
Another bag contains 1 red and 4 white beads.
A bead is selected at random from the first bag and placed in the second bag.
A bead is then selected at random from the second bag and placed in the first bag.

Draw a tree diagram and find the probability that the first bag still contains 2 red and 3 white beads.

Unit 4 Graphs

Reminder

To draw the graph of $y = 3x - 2$, we first complete a table of values like this

x	-2	-1	0	1	2
$3x$	-6	-3	0	3	6
-2	-2	-2	-2	-2	-2
y	-8	-5	-2	1	4

Then we draw axes, plot the points and, if all the points are on a straight line, join them with a ruler.

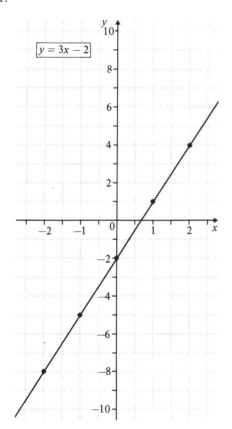

$y = 3x - 2$

Exercise 4.1

1 Draw a graph with an x-axis from -2 to $+2$ and a y-axis from -6 to $+6$.
Use a scale of 1 cm to 1 unit on both axes.
Draw up a table of values from $x = -2$ to $x = +2$ for each of the following equations and plot them on your graph.

  a $y = x + 3$ **b** $y = x + 2$ **c** $y = x + 1$
  d $y = x$ **e** $y = x - 1$ **f** $y = x - 2$
  g $y = x - 3$

2 Draw a graph with an x-axis from -2 to $+2$ and a y-axis from -6 to $+6$.
Use a scale of 1 cm to 1 unit on both axes.
Draw up a table of values from $x = -2$ to $x = +2$ for each of the following equations and plot them on your graph.

  a $y = 3x$ **b** $y = 2x$ **c** $y = x$
  d $y = -x$ **e** $y = -2x$ **f** $y = -3x$

3 Draw a graph with an x-axis from -2 to $+2$ and a y-axis from -10 to $+10$.
Use a scale of 1 cm to 1 unit on both axes.
Draw up a table of values from $x = -2$ to $x = +2$ for each of the following equations and plot them on your graph.

  a $y = 2x + 3$ **b** $y = 2x + 2$ **c** $y = 2x + 1$
  d $y = 2x - 1$ **e** $y = 2x - 2$ **f** $y = 2x - 3$

4 Draw a graph with a x-axis from -2 to $+2$ and a y-axis from -10 to $+10$.
Use a scale of 1 cm to 1 unit on both axes.
Draw up a table of values from $x = -2$ to $x = +2$ for each of the following equations and plot them on your graph.

  a $y = -3x + 3$ **b** $y = -3x + 2$
  c $y = -3x + 1$ **d** $y = -3x - 1$
  e $y = -3x - 2$ **f** $y = -3x - 3$

The *intercept* of a graph is the value of y at the point where the graph crosses the y-axis.

The *gradient (or slope)* of a graph can be measured between any two selected points on the graph.

$$\text{gradient} = \frac{\text{change in } y}{\text{change in } x}$$

Example 1

a Draw the graph of $y = 2x - 1$ for values of x from -2 to $+2$.
b Find the intercept of $y = 2x - 1$.
c Find the gradient of $y = 2x - 1$.

a

x	-2	-1	0	1	2
$2x$	-4	-2	0	2	4
-1	-1	-1	-1	-1	-1
y	-5	-3	-1	1	3

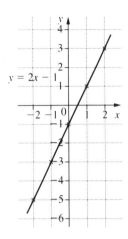

$y = 2x - 1$

b The graph crosses the y-axis at $(0, -1)$
Therefore, the intercept $= -1$

c The points $(1, 1)$ and $(2, 3)$ are selected (to avoid working with negative numbers).
Between the points $(1, 1)$ and $(2, 3)$

$$\text{gradient} = \frac{\text{change in } y}{\text{change in } x} = \frac{3 - 1}{2 - 1} = \frac{2}{1}$$

Example 2

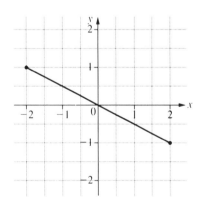

a Find the intercept of the graph.
b Find the gradient of the graph using the two points marked with dots.

a The intercept $= 0$

b Between the points $(-2, 1)$ and $(2, -1)$

$$\text{gradient} = \frac{\text{change in } y}{\text{change in } x} = \frac{-1 - 1}{2 - -2} = \frac{-2}{4} = \frac{-1}{2}$$

Finding the gradient of this graph involves difficult calculations with negative numbers. It may be easier to read the changes in x and y directly from the graph like this.

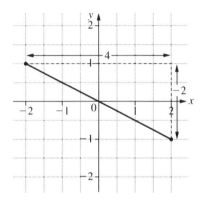

$$\text{gradient} = \frac{-2}{4} = \frac{-1}{2}$$

Exercise 4.2

In questions **1** to **20**

a find the intercept of the graph
b find the gradient of the graph using the two points marked with dots.

1

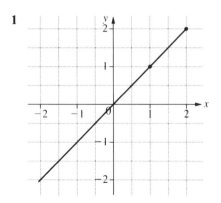

2

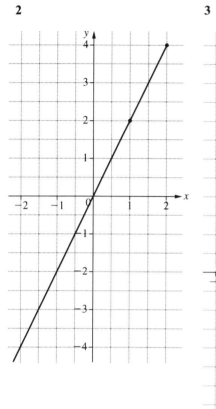

3

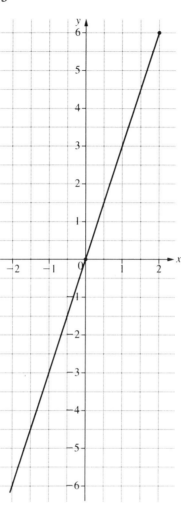

4

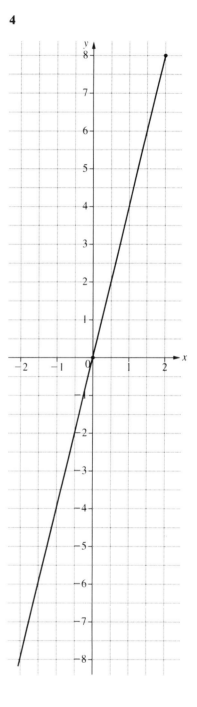

5

6

7

8

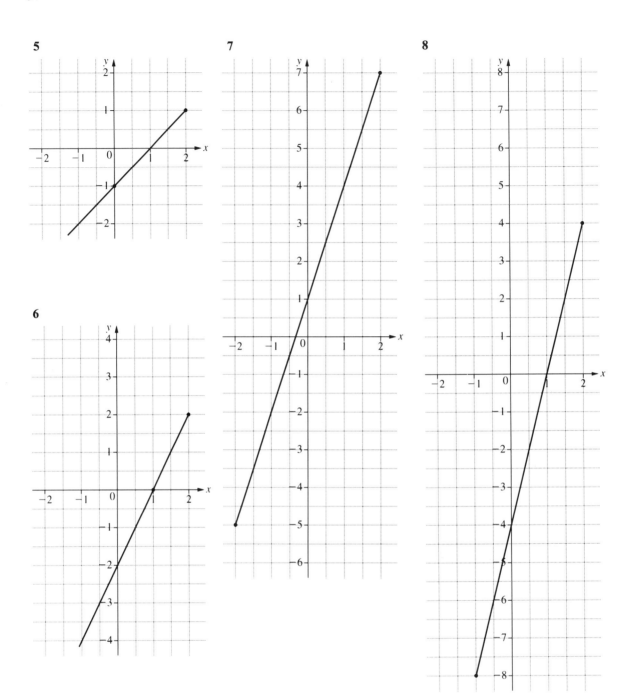

9

12

15

10

13

11

14

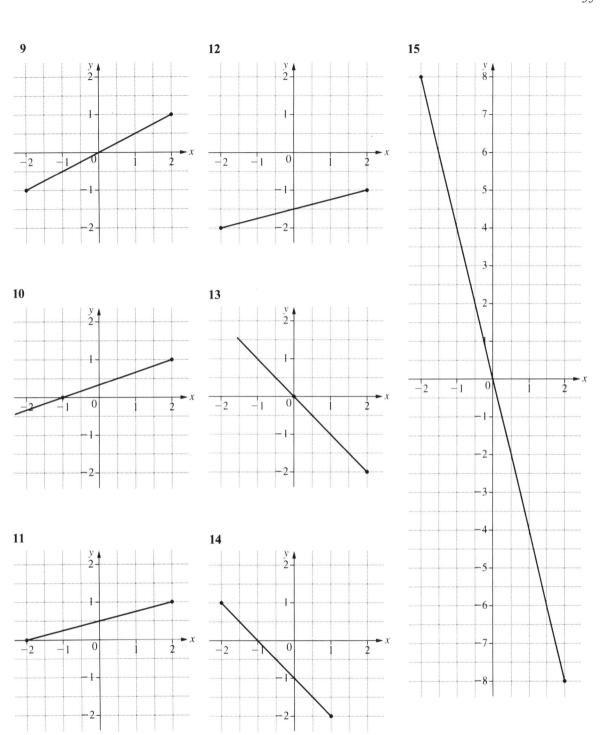

36

16
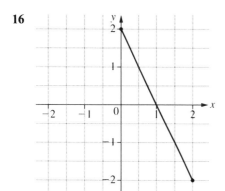

17
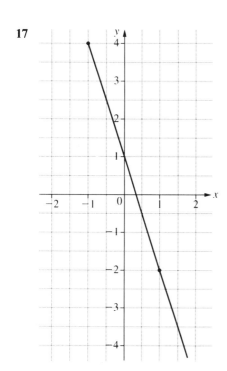

18
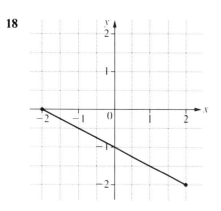

19
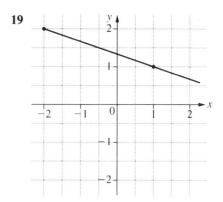

20
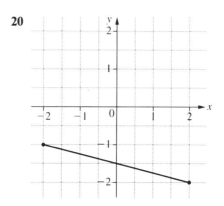

Exercise 4.3

In questions **1** to **20**, for each equation

a draw up a table of values from $x = -2$ to $x = +2$
b draw suitable axes and plot the graph of the equation
c find the intercept of the graph
d find the gradient of the graph.

1 $y = x + 6$ **2** $y = x - 4$
3 $y = 2x - 4$ **4** $y = 3x + 4$
5 $y = 4x + 3$ **6** $y = 4x - 2$
7 $y = 5x - 5$ **8** $y = 6 - 2x$
9 $y = 6 - 3x$ **10** $y = -4x - 1$

11 $y = -5x$ **12** $y = \dfrac{x}{2} + 1$

13 $y = \dfrac{x}{2} + 4$ **14** $y = \dfrac{x}{2} - 3$

15 $y = \dfrac{x}{4}$ **16** $y = \dfrac{x}{4} - 2$

17 $y = \dfrac{x}{4} + 4$ **18** $y = \dfrac{(x + 1)}{3}$

19 $y = \dfrac{(x + 2)}{4}$ **20** $y = \dfrac{(6 - 3x)}{3}$

If the equation of a graph is written in the form

$$y = mx + c$$

then the value of m will be the *gradient* of the graph and the value of c will be the *intercept* of the graph.

Example 3

a Write down the gradient and intercept of the graph with equation $y = 5x + 2$

b What is the equation of the graph with a gradient of 4 and an intercept of -7?

a gradient $= 5$ intercept $= 2$

b $y = 4x - 7$

Exercise 4.4

In questions **1** to **16**, write down the gradient and intercept of the graph of each equation.

1 $y = 4x + 5$	**2** $y = 4x - 5$
3 $y = 5x + 4$	**4** $y = 5x - 4$
5 $y = 4 - 5x$	**6** $y = 5 - 4x$
7 $y = -4x - 5$	**8** $y = -4 - 5x$
9 $y = 11x$	**10** $y = -13x$
11 $y = \dfrac{x}{3}$	**12** $y = \dfrac{-x}{5}$
13 $y = \dfrac{5x}{2}$	**14** $y = \dfrac{-7x}{2}$
15 $y = \dfrac{x}{5} + 3$	**16** $y = \dfrac{3x}{2} - 9$

In questions **17** to **32**, write down the equation of the graph with the given gradient and intercept.

17 gradient $= 3$	intercept $= 2$
18 gradient $= 3$	intercept $= -2$
19 gradient $= 2$	intercept $= 3$
20 gradient $= 2$	intercept $= -3$
21 gradient $= -3$	intercept $= 2$
22 gradient $= -3$	intercept $= -2$
23 gradient $= -2$	intercept $= 3$
24 gradient $= -2$	intercept $= -3$
25 gradient $= 7$	intercept $= 0$
26 gradient $= -4$	intercept $= 0$
27 gradient $= \frac{1}{4}$	intercept $= 0$
28 gradient $= \frac{5}{4}$	intercept $= 0$
29 gradient $= -\frac{1}{2}$	intercept $= 0$
30 gradient $= -\frac{1}{2}$	intercept $= 3$
31 gradient $= \frac{7}{2}$	intercept $= -5$
32 gradient $= -\frac{9}{5}$	intercept $= -8$

Curved graphs

The graph below shows the curve of the equation $y = x^2 - 4$.

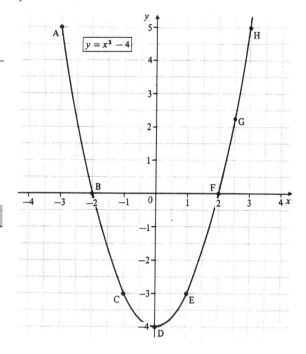

Example 4

The table below is to show the x-coordinate and the y-coordinate of each lettered point on the graph of $y = x^2 - 4$.

	A	B	C	D	E	F	G	H
x	-3			0	1			
y	5	0						

Copy and complete this table.

The completed table of values is as follows.

	A	B	C	D	E	F	G	H
x	-3	-2	-1	0	1	2	$2\frac{1}{2}$	3
y	5	0	-3	-4	-3	0	$2\frac{1}{4}$	5

38

For each question, copy and complete the table of values on the left so that it gives the coordinates of each lettered point on the graph of the equation.

1 $y = x^2$

	A	B	C	D	E	F
x	-2				$1\frac{1}{2}$	
y	4				$2\frac{1}{4}$	

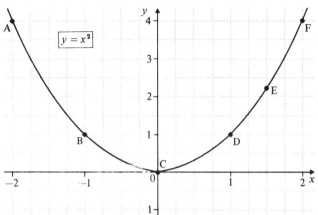

2 $y = x^2 - 1$

	A	B	C	D	E	F
x		-1	0	1		
y		0	-1	0		

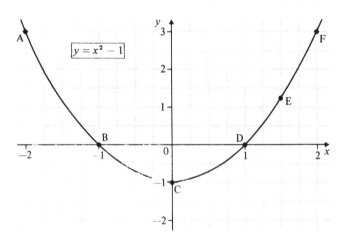

3 $y = x^2 - 6$

	A	B	C	D	E	F	G
x		-2			1		
y		-2			-5		

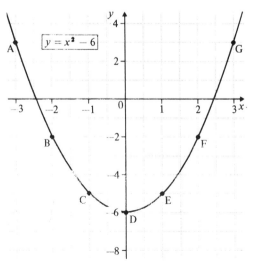

4 $y = x^2 - \frac{1}{4}$

	A	B	C	D	E	F	G	H	I
x	-2	$-1\frac{1}{2}$		$-\frac{1}{2}$	0				
y	$3\frac{3}{4}$	2		0	$-\frac{1}{4}$				

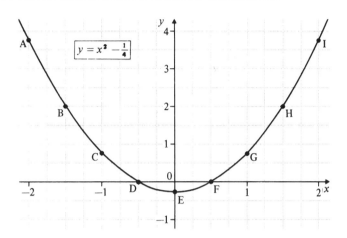

5 $y = 1 - x^2$

	A	B	C	D	E	F
x			0			
y			1			

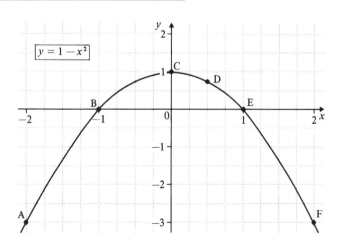

6 $y = 4 - x^2$

	A	B	C	D	E	F	G
x							
y							

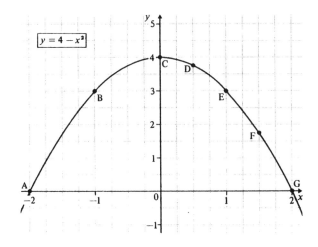

Example 5

Plot the graph of the curve $y = 2 - x^2$ from the following table of values.

x	−3	−2	−1	0	1	2	3
y	−7	−2	1	2	1	−2	−7

Use a scale of 1 cm to 1 unit on the x-axis and a scale of 1 cm to 2 units on the y-axis.

Your completed graph should look like this.

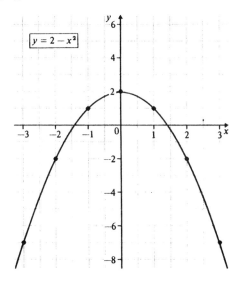

Exercise 4.6

For each question, use the table of values to plot the graph of the equation.
Use a scale of 1 cm to 1 unit on the x-axis and a scale of 1 cm to 2 units on the y-axis.

1 $y = x^2 - 2$

x	−3	−2	−1	0	1	2	3
y	7	2	−1	−2	−1	2	7

2 $y = x^2 - 3$

x	−3	−2	−1	0	1	2	3
y	6	1	−2	−3	−2	1	6

3 $y = x^2 - 5$

x	−3	−2	−1	0	1	2	3
y	4	−1	−4	−5	−4	−1	4

4 $y = 3 - x^2$

x	−3	−2	−1	0	1	2	3
y	−6	−1	2	3	2	−1	−6

5 $y = 5 - x^2$

x	−3	−2	−1	0	1	2	3
y	−4	1	4	5	4	1	−4

6 $y = 7 - x^2$

x	−3	−2	−1	0	1	2	3
y	−2	3	6	7	6	3	−2

For every graph of an equation we have to draw up a table of values, as shown below.

Example 6

Draw up a table of values for the equation $y = x^2 + 2$ for values of x from +3 to −3.

	values of x	−3	−2	−1	0	1	2	3
working	x^2	+9	+4	+1	0	+1	+4	+9
	+2	+2	+2	+2	+2	+2	+2	+2
	values of y	+11	+6	+3	+2	+3	+6	+11

Note that, when $x = -3$, $x^2 = -3 \times -3 = +9$
and $y = x^2 + 2 = 9 + 2 = 11$

and so on...

Exercise 4.7

Copy and complete each table of values.
Do not draw the graph.

1 $y = x^2 + 1$

x	−3	−2	−1	0	1	2	3
x^2							
+1							
y							

2 $y = x^2 + 3$

x	−3	−2	−1	0	1	2	3
x^2							
+3							
y							

3 $y = x^2 + 6$

x	−3	−2	−1	0	1	2	3
x^2							
+6							
y							

4 $y = x^2 - 7$

x	−3	−2	−1	0	1	2	3
x^2							
−7							
y							

5 $x = x^2 - 9$

x	−3	−2	−1	0	1	2	3
x^2							
−9							
y							

6 $y = 8 - x^2$

x	−3	−2	−1	0	1	2	3
+8							
$-x^2$							
y							

7 $y = 4 - x^2$

x	−3	−2	−1	0	1	2	3
+4							
−x²							
y							

8 $y = 1 - x^2$

x	−3	−2	−1	0	1	2	3
+1							
−x²							
y							

Example 7

Copy and complete the following table of values for the relationship $y = x^2 + 2x$.

working $\left\{ \vphantom{\begin{matrix}a\\b\\c\end{matrix}} \right.$

values of x	−3	−2	−1	0	1
x²	+9		+1	0	+1
+2x	−6	−4		0	
values of y	+3			0	

Then plot the graph using a scale of 1 cm to 1 unit on both axes.

To find the missing values on the table.

When $x = -2$, $x^2 = +4$ and $2x = -4$;
so $y = x^2 + 2x = +4 - 4 = 0$

When $x = -1$, $x^2 = +1$ and $2x = -2$;
so $y = x^2 + 2x = +1 + -2 = -1$

When $x = 1$, $x^2 = +1$ and $2x = +2$;
so $y = x^2 + 2x = +1 + 2 = +3$

values of x	−3	−2	−1	0	1
x²	+9	+4	+1	0	+1
+2x	−6	−4	−2	0	+2
values of y	+3	0	−1	0	+3

Your completed graph should look like this.

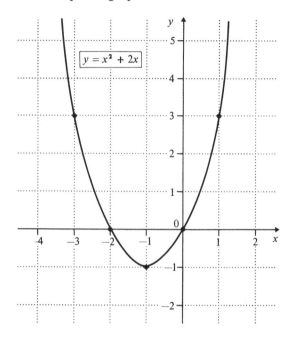

$y = x^2 + 2x$

Exercise 4.8

For each question, copy and complete the table of values.
Then plot the graph of the relationship using a scale of 1 cm to 1 unit on both axes.

1 $y = x^2 + 4x$

x	−5	−4	−3	−2	−1	0	1
x²	+25	+16		+4		0	+1
+4x	−20	−16	−12			0	
y	+5	0				0	

2 $y = x^2 + 3x$

x	−4	−3	−2	−1	0	1
x²		+9		+1		+1
+3x	−12			−3		
y			−2			

3 $y = x^2 + 5x$

x	−6	−5	−4	−3	−2	−1	0	1
x²	+36			+9		0		
+5x		−25		−15				
y				−6				

4 $y = x^2 + x$

x	-3	-2	-1	0	1	2
x^2	$+9$				$+4$	
$+x$	-3				$+2$	
y	$+6$				$+6$	

5 $y = 4x - x^2$

x	-1	0	1	2	3	4	5
$+4x$	-4		$+4$				$+20$
$-x^2$	-1	0			-4		-25
y	-5						-5

6 $y = 2x - x^2$

x	-1	0	1	2	3
$+2x$					$+6$
$-x^2$			-1		
y					

7 $y = 3x - x^2$

x	-1	0	1	2	3	4
$+3x$						
$-x^2$						
y						

8 $y = x^2 - 2x$

x	-1	0	1	2	3
x^2					
$-2x$					
y					

9 $y = x^2 - 3x$

x	-1	0	1	2	3	4
x^2						
$-3x$						
y						

10 $y = x^2 - 2x$

x	-2	-1	0	1	2	3
x^2						
$-x$						
y						

Example 8

Draw the graph of $y = \dfrac{12}{x}$ for values of x from -6 to 6.

First, we construct a table.

x	-6	-5	-4	-3	-2	-1	0	1	2	3	4	5	6
y	-2	-2.4	-3	-4	-6	-12		$+12$	$+6$	$+4$	$+3$	$+2.4$	$+2$

In the table a gap is left under the zero. This is because $12 \div 0$ is infinitely large.

No value of the equation can therefore be plotted above or below zero on the x-axis.
The graph is split into two halves, one to the left and one to the right of the y-axis.

44

This is the graph.

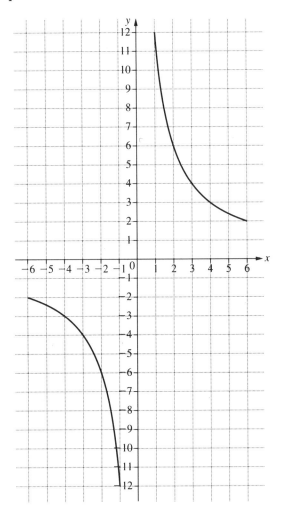

1 Draw the graph of $y = \dfrac{6}{x}$ for values of x from -6 to 6.

2 Draw the graph of $y = \dfrac{24}{x}$ for values of x from -6 to 6.

3 a Copy and complete this table for the equation $y = \dfrac{12}{x} + 5$

x	-6	-5	-4	-3	-2	-1	0	1	2	3	4	5	6
$\dfrac{12}{x}$	-2	-2.4	-3	-4	-6	-12		$+12$	$+6$	$+4$	$+3$	$+2.4$	$+2$
$+5$	$+5$			$+5$				$+5$			$+5$		
y	$+3$	$+2.6$				-7		$+17$		$+9$			$+7$

b Draw the graph of the equation.

4 a Copy and complete this table for the equation $y = \dfrac{6}{x} - 6$

x	-6	-5	-4	-3	-2	-1	0	1	2	3	4	5	6
$\dfrac{6}{x}$	-1		-1.5		-3			$+6$		$+2$		$+1.2$	
-6	-6		-6			-6			-6		-6		-6
y	-7	-7.2			-9			0					-5

b Draw the graph of the equation.

5 a Copy and complete this table for the equation $y = 10 - \dfrac{8}{x}$

x	-6	-5	-4	-3	-2	-1	0	1	2	3	4	5	6
$+10$	$+10$		$+10$		$+10$			$+10$		$+10$			$+10$
$\dfrac{-8}{x}$	$+1.3$	$+1.6$	$+2$			$+8$		-8	-4	-2.7			-1.3
y	$+11.3$	$+11.6$		$+12.7$	$+14$	$+18$		$+2$	$+6$		$+8$	$+8.4$	

b Draw the graph of the equation.

6 a Copy and complete this table for the equation $y = \dfrac{12}{x} + x$

x	-6	-5	-4	-3	-2	-1	0	1	2	3	4	5	6
$\dfrac{12}{x}$	-2	-2.4	-3	-4	-6	-12		$+12$	$+6$	$+4$	$+3$	$+2.4$	$+2$
$+x$	-6	-5			-2			$+1$		$+3$	$+4$		
y	-8	-7.4	-7		-8	-13		$+13$		$+7$	$+7$		$+8$

b Draw the graph of the equation.

Example 9

Draw the graph of $y = x^3$ for values of x from -4 to 4.

First, we construct a table.

x	-4	-3	-2	-1	0	1	2	3	4
y	-64	-27	-8	-1	0	$+1$	$+8$	$+27$	$+64$

This is the graph.

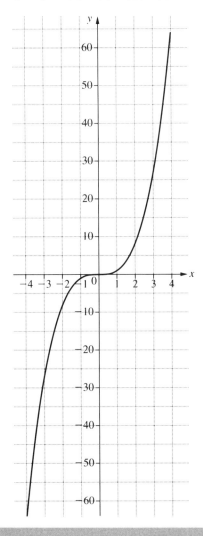

Exercise 4.10

1 a Copy and complete this table for the equation $y = x^3 - 12x$

x	-4	-3	-2	-1	0	1	2	3	4
x^3	-64	-27	-8	-1	0	$+1$	$+8$	$+27$	$+64$
$-12x$	$+48$	$+36$		$+12$	0	-12	-24		-48
y	-16		$+16$	$+11$		-11		-9	$+16$

b Draw the graph of the equation.

2 a Copy and complete this table for the equation $y = x^3 - 27x$

x	-4	-3	-2	-1	0	1	2	3	4
x^3	-64	-27	-8	-1	0	$+1$	$+8$	$+27$	$+64$
$-27x$	$+108$		$+54$		0	-27		-81	
y	$+44$			$+26$	0	-26		-54	

b Draw the graph of the equation.

3 a Copy and complete this table for the equation $y = x^3 + 3x^2$

x	-4	-3	-2	-1	0	1	2
x^3	-64	-27	-8	-1	0	$+1$	$+8$
$+3x^2$	$+48$		$+12$	$+3$	0		
y	-16	0	$+4$		0		$+20$

b Draw the graph of the equation.

4 a Copy and complete this table for the equation $y = x^3 + 4x^2 + 4x$

x	-4	-3	-2	-1	0	1
x^3	-64	-27	-8	-1	0	$+1$
$+4x^2$	$+64$	$+36$			0	$+4$
$+4x$	-16			-4	0	
y	-16	-3			0	

b Draw the graph of the equation.

Exercise 4.11

1 A vet uses the rule $w = 0.9d + 1.7$ to estimate the weight (w kg) a piglet should be d days from birth.
  a Complete a table of values for $w = 0.9d + 1.7$ as d takes values from 0 to 10.
  b Draw a graph of the equation $w = 0.9d + 1.7$
  c What is the intercept of the graph?
  Explain the intercept in terms of a newborn piglet.
  d What is the gradient of the graph?
  Explain the gradient in terms of a newborn piglet.

2 A newspaper uses the rule $C = 2L + 1.5$ to estimate the cost (£C) of an advertisement L lines long.
  a Complete a table of values for $C = 2L + 1.5$ as L takes values from 0 to 10.
  b Draw a graph of the equation $C = 2L + 1.5$
  c What is the intercept of the graph?
  Explain the intercept in terms of an advertisement.
  d What is the gradient of the graph?
  Explain the gradient in terms of an advertisement.

3 The depth of water in a well can be found by dropping a stone and timing how many seconds it takes to hit the water.

The approximate depth of the well in metres is found from the formula

$$d = 5t^2$$

where d is the depth in metres and t is the time in seconds.

a Complete a table of values for $d = 5t^2$ taking values of t from 0 to 4.

b Draw a graph of the equation $d = 5t^2$

c Use your graph to estimate the depth of a well if a dropped stone takes 2.5 seconds to hit the water.

d Use your graph to estimate the time a dropped stone takes to hit the water in a well 60 m deep.

4 A rectangle is formed from a loop of string 24 cm long.

a Copy and complete this table showing the height (h), width (w) and area (a) of different rectangles that could be formed from the string.

h (cm)	12	11	10	9	8	7	6	5	4	3	2	1	0
w (cm)	0	1	2		4	5		7	8			11	12
a (cm²)	0	11		27			36	35			20		

b A farmer has 24 m of fencing with which to build a rectangular pen for some sheep.

What is the maximum area for the pen?

5 A company which makes wooden fencing panels receives an order for 1200 panels. Each worker can make 50 panels a day.

a If W workers are used to complete the order and it takes D days, explain why

$$D = \frac{24}{W}$$

b Copy and complete this table.

W	1	2	3	4	5	6	7	8	9	10	11	12
D	24		8		4.8		3.4		2.7			2

c Draw the graph of $D = \dfrac{24}{W}$

d How many workers will be needed to complete the order in less than 3 days?

Unit 5　Right-angled triangles

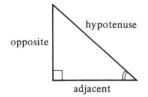

In any right-angled triangle, the side opposite the right angle is called the *hypotenuse*.

If a second angle in the triangle is marked, the other two sides are named as follows

a the *opposite* side is opposite the marked angle
b the *adjacent* side is next to the marked angle.

The three sides of the right-angled triangle are named hypotenuse, opposite and adjacent.

Example 1

a 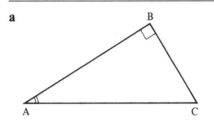　**b**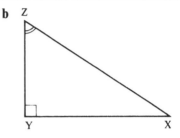

Name the sides of each triangle.

a AC is the hypotenuse; BC is the opposite side to A; and AB is the adjacent side to A.
b ZX is the hypotenuse; XY is the opposite side to Z; and YZ is the adjacent side to Z.

Example 2

Look at the triangles below.

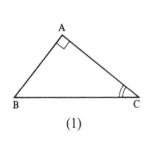　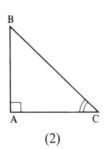　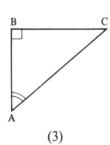　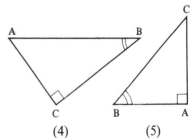

(1)　　　　　(2)　　　　　(3)　　　　　(4)　　　　　(5)

In which triangle is the side AC

a the opposite side
b the adjacent side
c the hypotenuse?

a AC is the opposite side in (4) and (5)
b AC is the adjacent side in (1) and in (2)
c AC is the hypotenuse in (3).

Exercise 5.1

1 In which of these five triangles is the side AC
   a the opposite side
   b the adjacent side
   c the hypotenuse?

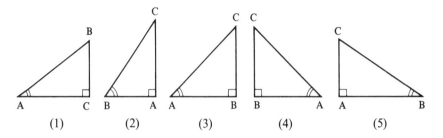

2 In which of these five triangles is the side XZ
   a the opposite side
   b the adjacent side
   c the hypotenuse?

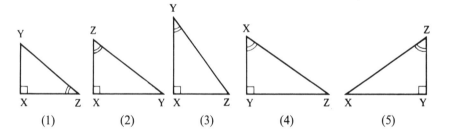

3 In which of these five triangles is the side PR
   a the opposite side
   b the adjacent side
   c the hypotenuse?

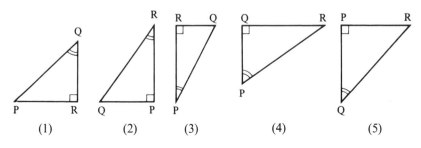

4 In which of these five triangles is the side LN
   a the opposite side
   b the adjacent side
   c the hypotenuse?

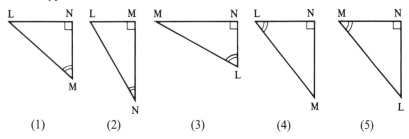

(1)   (2)   (3)   (4)   (5)

5 In which of these five triangles is the side BD
   a the opposite side
   b the adjacent side
   c the hypotenuse?

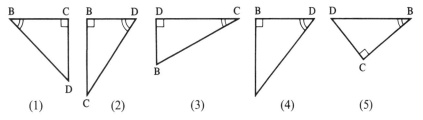

(1)   (2)   (3)   (4)   (5)

6 In which of these five triangles is the side RT
   a the opposite side
   b the adjacent side
   c the hypotenuse?

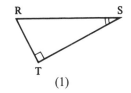 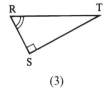 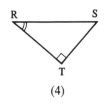 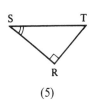

(1)   (2)   (3)   (4)   (5)

7 In which of these five triangles is the side UW
   a the opposite side
   b the adjacent side
   c the hypotenuse?

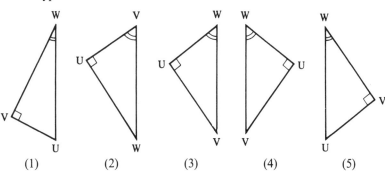

(1)   (2)   (3)   (4)   (5)

52

8 In which of these five triangles is the side DF
  a the opposite side
  b the adjacent side
  c the hypotenuse?

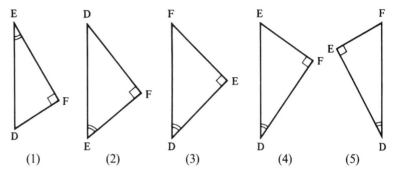

   (1)   (2)   (3)   (4)   (5)

9 In which of these five triangles is the side KM
  a the opposite side
  b the adjacent side
  c the hypotenuse?

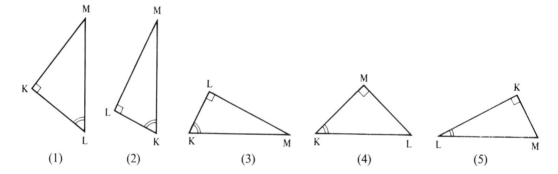

   (1)   (2)   (3)   (4)   (5)

Exercise 5.2

In each of these four right-angled triangles, $\widehat{A} = 90°$, $\widehat{B} = 60°$ and $\widehat{C} = 30°$.
Measure the sides carefully, and then copy and complete the table.

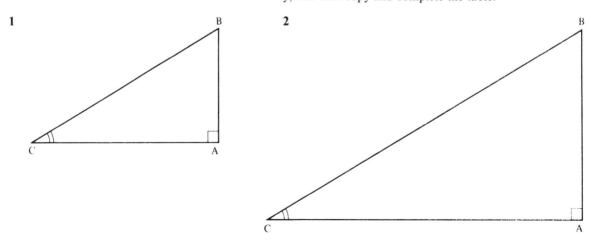

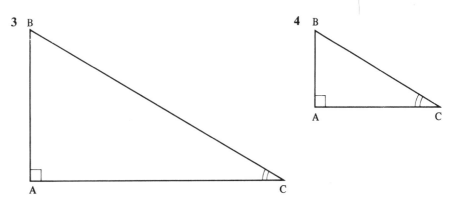

triangle	size of $\widehat{C}$	length of side opposite C	length of hypotenuse	$\dfrac{\text{length of opposite}}{\text{length of hypotenuse}}$
1	30°	3 cm	6 cm	$\frac{3}{6} = \frac{1}{2} = 0.5$
2	30°		10 cm	
3	30°	4 cm		
4	30°			

Sine, cosine and tangent

If you have made accurate measurements in Exercise 5.2, you should have found in each question that

$$\text{the ratio} \quad \frac{\text{length of opposite}}{\text{length of hypotenuse}} = \tfrac{1}{2} \text{ or } 0.5$$

This ratio is called the *sine* ratio. Each angle has its own special value for the sine ratio.

e.g.   30° has the sine ratio of 0.50. This is written $\sin 30° = 0.50$
       70° has the sine ratio of 0.94. This is written $\sin 70° = 0.94$

Example 3

Write down the sine ratio of
a $\widehat{B}$ in triangle ABC   **b** $Y\widehat{X}Z$ in triangle XYZ

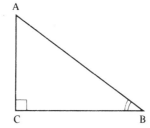

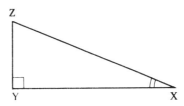

In triangle ABC,
AC is the side opposite angle B;
AB is the hypotenuse.

In triangle XYZ,
YZ is the side opposite angle YXZ;
XZ is the hypotenuse.

$$\text{so, sin B} = \frac{\text{length of opposite}}{\text{length of hypotenuse}} \qquad \text{so, sin XYZ} = \frac{\text{length of opposite}}{\text{length of hypotenuse}}$$

$$= \frac{\text{AC}}{\text{AB}} \qquad\qquad\qquad = \frac{\text{YZ}}{\text{XZ}}$$

Exercise 5.3

For questions **1** to **12**, write down the sine ratio of the marked angle.

1 A B C

2 X Y Z

3 P Q R

4 L N M

5 U W V

6 B D C

7 R T S

8 K M L

9 D E F

10 T U V

11 B D C

12 S Q R

13 In which triangle is the sine ration of $\widehat{Y}$ *not* equal to $\dfrac{XZ}{XY}$?

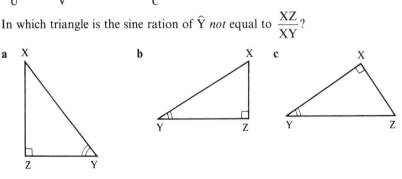

a X Z Y   **b** X Y Z   **c** X Y Z

14 In which triangle is the sine ratio of $\widehat{Q}$ *not* equal to $\dfrac{PR}{PQ}$?

a

b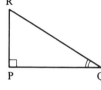

c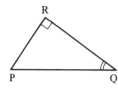

The ratio $\dfrac{\text{length of adjacent}}{\text{length of hypotenuse}}$ is called the *cosine* ratio.

Each angle has its own special value for the cosine ratio.

e.g.   30° has a cosine ratio of 0.866. This is written cos 30° = 0.866

20° has a cosine ratio of 0.940. This is written cos 20° = 0.940

Example 4

Write down the cosine ratio of $\widehat{A}$.

AB is the side adjacent to angle A;
AC is the hypotenuse.

so, $\cos A = \dfrac{\text{length of adjacent}}{\text{length of hypotenuse}} = \dfrac{AB}{AC}$

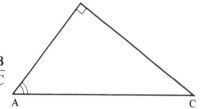

Exercise 5.4

For questions **1** to **12**, write down the cosine ratio of the marked angle.

1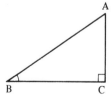

2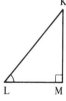

3

4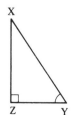

5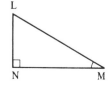

6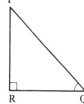

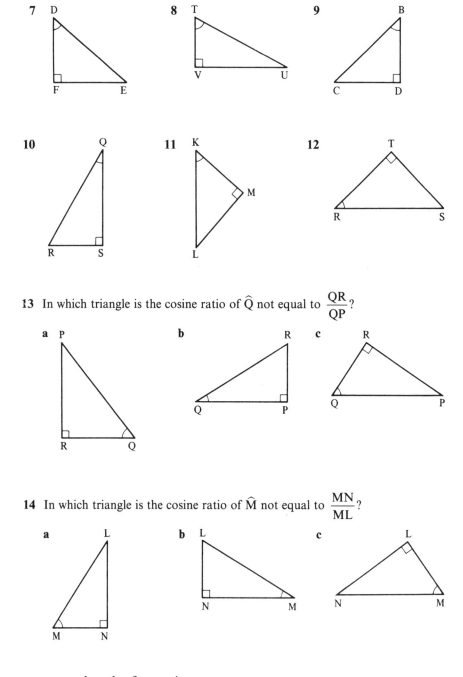

13 In which triangle is the cosine ratio of $\widehat{Q}$ not equal to $\dfrac{QR}{QP}$?

14 In which triangle is the cosine ratio of $\widehat{M}$ not equal to $\dfrac{MN}{ML}$?

The ratio $\dfrac{\text{length of opposite}}{\text{length of adjacent}}$ is called the *tangent* ratio.

Each angle has its own special value for the tangent ratio.

e.g.   35° has a tangent ratio of 0.70. This is written tan 35° = 0.70

45° has a tangent ratio of 1.00. This is written tan 45° = 1.00

58° has a tangent ratio of 1.60. This is written tan 58° = 1.60

Example 5

Write down the tangent of $\widehat{Z}$.

XY is the side opposite to angle Z
XZ is the side adjacent to angle Z

so, $\tan Z = \dfrac{\text{length of opposite}}{\text{length of adjacent}} = \dfrac{XY}{XZ}$

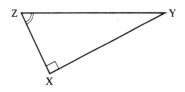

Exercise 5.5

For questions **1** to **12**, write down the tangent ratio of the marked angle.

1

2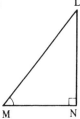

3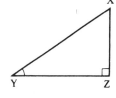

4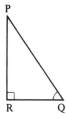

5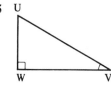

6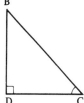

7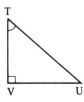

8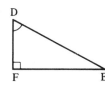

9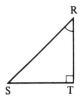

10

11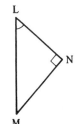

12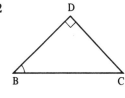

Using sines

The table on the right gives the sine ratio of any angle A° from 0° to 90°.

Example 6

Find the sine ratio of an angle of 43°.

From the table (——→), sin 43° = 0.682

Example 7

Find the size of the angle whose sine ratio is 0.469.

From the table (- - - →), sin 28° = 0.469, so the size of the angle is 28°.

Exercise 5.6

Find the sine ratio of the following angles.

1 20°	**2** 30°	**3** 50°	**4** 60°
5 15°	**6** 35°	**7** 65°	**8** 85°
9 5°	**10** 8°	**11** 12°	**12** 27°
13 41°	**14** 66°	**15** 83°	

Find the size of the angle for the following sine ratios.

16 0.174	**17** 0.643	**18** 0.940	**19** 0.985
20 0.423	**21** 0.707	**22** 0.819	**23** 0.966
24 0.052	**25** 0.156	**26** 0.375	**27** 0.616
28 0.857	**29** 0.974	**30** 0.995	

The sine ratio can be used in right-angled triangles to find
a the length of the side *opposite* to a given angle if the length of the hypotenuse is known
b the size of an angle if the length of the hypotenuse and the length of the side *opposite* to this angle are known.

Table of sines

A°	sin A	A°	sin A
0	0.000	45	0.707
1	0.017	46	0.719
2	0.035	47	0.731
3	0.052	48	0.743
4	0.070	49	0.755
5	0.087	50	0.766
6	0.105	51	0.777
7	0.122	52	0.788
8	0.139	53	0.799
9	0.156	54	0.809
10	0.174	55	0.819
11	0.191	56	0.829
12	0.208	57	0.839
13	0.225	58	0.848
14	0.242	59	0.857
15	0.259	60	0.866
16	0.276	61	0.875
17	0.292	62	0.883
18	0.309	63	0.891
19	0.326	64	0.899
20	0.342	65	0.906
21	0.358	66	0.914
22	0.375	67	0.921
23	0.391	68	0.927
24	0.407	69	0.934
25	0.423	70	0.940
26	0.438	71	0.946
27	0.454	72	0.951
28	0.469	73	0.956
29	0.485	74	0.961
30	0.500	75	0.966
31	0.515	76	0.970
32	0.530	77	0.974
33	0.545	78	0.978
34	0.559	79	0.982
35	0.574	80	0.985
36	0.588	81	0.988
37	0.602	82	0.990
38	0.616	83	0.993
39	0.629	84	0.995
40	0.643	85	0.996
41	0.656	86	0.998
42	0.669	87	0.999
43	0.682	88	0.999
44	0.695	89	1.000
		90	1.000

Example 8

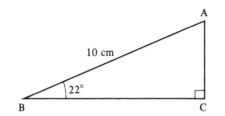

Find the length of AC.

AC is the side opposite to 22°;
AB is the hypotenuse.

ratio $\dfrac{\text{length of opposite}}{\text{length of hypotenuse}} = \sin 22°$

so, $\dfrac{\text{AC}}{\text{AB}} = \sin 22° = 0.375$

$\dfrac{\text{AC}}{10} = 0.375$

Multiply both sides by 10

$\text{AC} = 0.375 \times 10 = 3.75$

Hence AC is 3.75 cm long.

Exercise 5.7

For each triangle, find the length of AC.

1

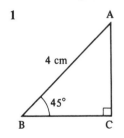

2

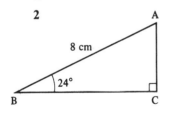

3

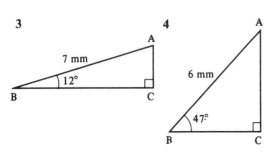

5

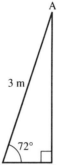

6

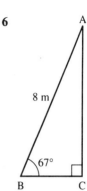

7

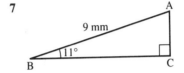

8

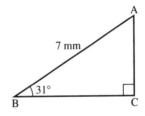

9

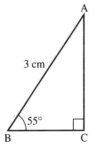

10

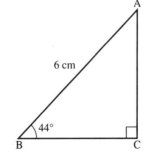

60

Example 9

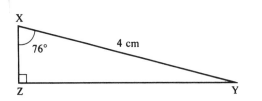

Find the length of YZ.

YZ is the side opposite to 76°
YX is the hypotenuse.

ratio $\dfrac{\text{length of opposite}}{\text{length of hypotenuse}} = \sin 76°$

so, $\dfrac{YZ}{YX} = 0.970$

$\dfrac{YZ}{4} = 0.970$

Multiply both sides by 4

$YZ = 0.970 \times 4 = 3.880$

Hence YZ is 3.88 cm long.

Exercise 5.8

For each triangle, find the length of YZ.

1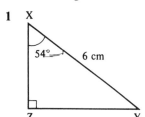

2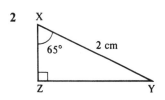

3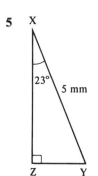

4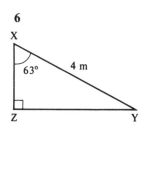

5

6

7

8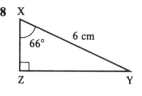

9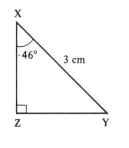

10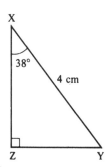

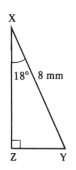

Example 10

A ladder 3.5 m long rests against a wall, making an angle of 75° with the ground.

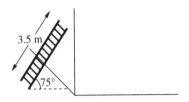

How far up the wall does the ladder reach?

The ladder, wall and ground form a right-angled triangle. If we let x represent the distance up the wall, we have

$$\frac{x}{3.5} = \sin 75° = 0.966$$

$$\frac{x}{3.5} = 0.966$$

Multiply both sides by 3.5

$$x = 0.966 \times 3.5 = 3.381$$

Hence the ladder reaches 3.381 m up the wall.

Exercise 5.9

1 A plane takes off and climbs at an angle of 40°.

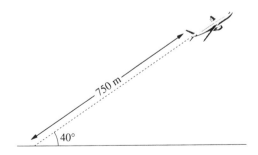

How high is the plane after it has flown 750 m through the air?

2 Norwich is 44 km on a bearing of 055° from Thetford.

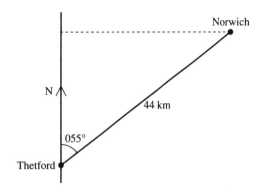

How far is Thetford to the west of Norwich?

3 A flagpole is supported by wires attached to the ground.

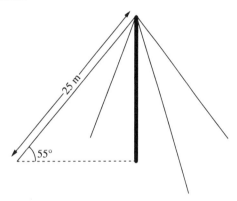

If each wire is 25 m long and meets the ground at an angle of 55°, how tall is the flagpole?

4 A see-saw is 3.6 m long and one end is touching the ground and making an angle of 32°.

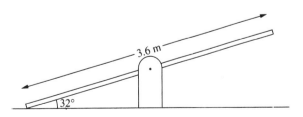

How high is the other end of the see-saw?

5 A ship leaves harbour and sails for 65 km on a bearing of 080°.

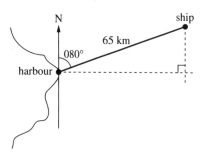

How far is the ship to the east of the harbour?

6 A clock pendulum 50 cm long swings through an angle of 40°.

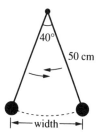

Calculate the width of the pendulum's swing.

7 A step ladder has legs 1.6 m long which meet at an angle of 25°.

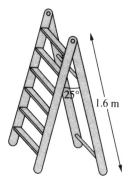

What is the distance between the feet of the step ladder?

8 A roof has sloping sides 4.2 m long which meet in the middle at an angle of 120°.

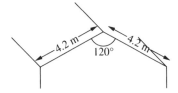

How wide is the house?

9 Each leg of a pair of compasses is 10 cm long.

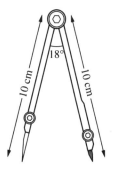

What is the radius of the circle the compasses will draw when the angle between the legs is 18°?

10 Susan and Siloben are sitting in a chair on the Big Wheel at a fairground. The Big Wheel has a radius of 10 m and their chair makes an angle of 20° with the horizontal.

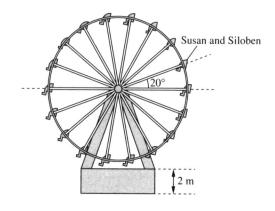

How high are Susan and Siloben?

Example 11

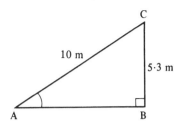

Find the size of $\widehat{A}$.

BC is the side opposite to the required angle, $\widehat{A}$; AC is the hypotenuse.

ratio $\dfrac{\text{length of opposite}}{\text{length of hypotenuse}} = \sin A$

so, $\sin A = \dfrac{BC}{AC} = \dfrac{5.3}{10} = 0.53$

$\sin A = 0.53$

From the table of sines on page 58, the size of the angle whose sine is 0.53 is 32°.

Hence $\widehat{A} = 32°$.

Exercise 5.10

For each triangle, find the size of $\widehat{A}$.

1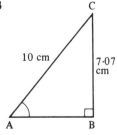

2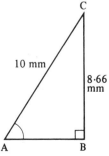

3

4

5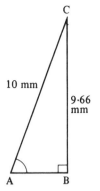

6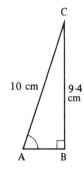

7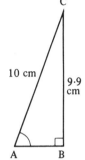

8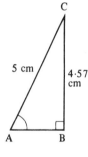

9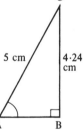

10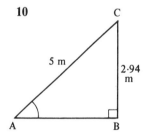

Example 12

Find the size of $\widehat{Z}$.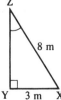

XY is the side opposite to $\widehat{Z}$; XZ is the hypotenuse.

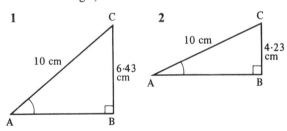

ratio $\dfrac{\text{length of opposite}}{\text{length of hypotenuse}} = \sin Z$

so, $\sin Z = \dfrac{XY}{XZ} = \dfrac{3}{8} = 0.375$

$\sin Z = 0.375$

From the table of sines on page 58 the size of the angle whose sine is 0.375 is 22°.

Hence $\widehat{Z} = 22°$.

Exercise 5.11

For each triangle, find the size of $\widehat{Z}$.

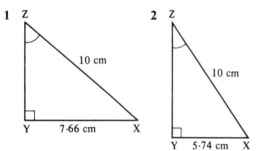

1 Z, 10 cm, Y 7·66 cm X

2 Z, 10 cm, Y 5·74 cm X

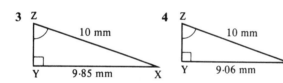

3 Z, 10 mm, Y 9·85 mm X

4 Z, 10 mm, Y 9·06 mm X

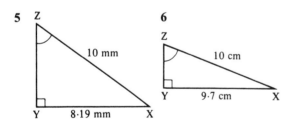

5 Z, 10 mm, Y 8·19 mm X

6 Z, 10 cm, Y 9·7 cm X

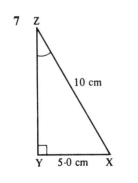

7 Z, 10 cm, Y 5·0 cm X

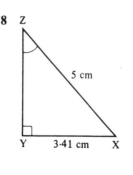

8 Z, 5 cm, Y 3·41 cm X

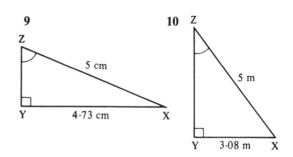

9 Z, 5 cm, Y 4·73 cm X

10 Z, 5 m, Y 3·08 m X

Example 13

A ladder 4.5 m long rests against a wall, reaching 2.5 m up the wall.

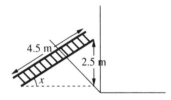

What angle does the foot of the ladder make with the ground?

The ladder, wall and ground form a right-angled triangle. If we let X represent the angle between the ground and the wall we have

$$\sin X = \dfrac{2.5}{4.5} = 0.556 \ \text{(correct to 3 dp)}$$

From the table of sines on page 58 the size of the angle whose sine is closest to 0.556 is 34°.

Hence the ladder meets the ground at an angle of 34° (correct to the nearest degree).

Exercise 5.12

1 A plane takes off and flies 900 m. It is then 500 m high.

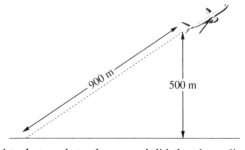

900 m / 500 m

At what angle to the ground did the plane climb?

2 The distance from Knutsford to Nantwich is 27 km and Knutsford is 10 km to the east of Nantwich.

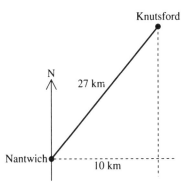

What is the bearing of Knutsford from Nantwich?

3 A flagpole 12 m high is supported by wires attached to the ground.
If each wire is 15 m long at what angle do the wires meet the ground?

4 A see-saw is 3.6 m long. One end is touching the ground and the other end is 1.2 m high.
At what angle does the see-saw meet the ground?

5 A ship leaves harbour and sails for 65 km. It is then 30 km East of the harbour.

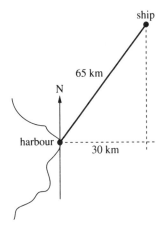

On what bearing did the ship sail?

6 A clock pendulum 50 cm long swings through an arc 24 cm wide.

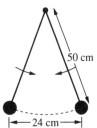

Through what angle does the pendulum swing?

7 A step ladder has legs 1.6 m long. The feet of the step ladder are 0.8 m apart.
What is the angle between the legs of the step ladder?

8 A roof with a width of 6 m has sloping sides 4.2 m long.

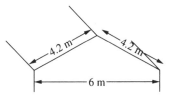

At what angle do the sloping sides of the roof meet?

9 Each leg of a pair of compasses is 10 cm long.
What is the angle between the legs of the compasses when it draws a circle of radius 5 cm?

10 Susan and Siloben are sitting in a chair on the Big Wheel at a fairground. They are 15.6 m high. The Big Wheel has a radius of 10 m.

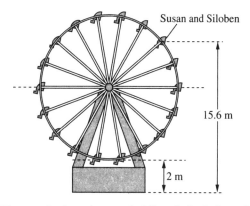

What angle does the arm holding their chair make with the horizontal?

Using cosines

The table on the right gives the cosine ratio of any angle B° from 0° to 90°.

Table of cosines

B°	cos B		B°	cos B
0	1.000		45	0.707
1	1.000		46	0.695
2	0.999		47	0.682
3	0.999		48	0.669
4	0.998		49	0.656
5	0.996		50	0.643
6	0.995		51	0.629
7	0.993		52	0.616
8	0.990		53	0.602
9	0.988		54	0.588
10	0.985		55	0.574
11	0.982		56	0.559
12	0.978	⟶	57	0.545 ⟵
13	0.974		58	0.530
14	0.970		59	0.515
15	0.966		60	0.500
16	0.961		61	0.485
17	0.956		62	0.469
18	0.951		63	0.454
19	0.946		64	0.438
20	0.940		65	0.423
21	0.934		66	0.407
22	0.927		67	0.391
23	0.921		68	0.375
24	0.914		69	0.358
25	0.906		70	0.342
26	0.899		71	0.326
27	0.891		72	0.309
28	0.883		73	0.292
29	0.875		74	0.276
30	0.866		75	0.259
31	0.857		76	0.242
32	0.848		77	0.225
33	0.839		78	0.208
34	0.829		79	0.191
35	0.819		80	0.174
36	0.809		81	0.156
37	0.799		82	0.139
38	0.788		83	0.122
⟶ 39	0.777 ⟵		84	0.105
40	0.766		85	0.087
41	0.755		86	0.070
42	0.743		87	0.052
43	0.731		88	0.035
44	0.719		89	0.017
			90	0.000

Example 14

Find the cosine ratio of an angle of 57°.
From the table (⟶), cos 57° = 0.545

Example 15

Find the size of the angle whose cosine ratio is 0.777.
From the table (- - - ⟶), cos 39° = 0.777, so the size of the angle is 39°.

Exercise 5.13

Find the cosine ratio of the following angles.

1 10°	**2** 30°	**3** 60°	**4** 70°
5 15°	**6** 25°	**7** 45°	**8** 65°
9 75°	**10** 7°	**11** 9°	**12** 29°
13 48°	**14** 62°	**15** 86°	

Find the size of the angle for the following cosine ratios.

16 0.940	**17** 0.766	**18** 0.643	**19** 0.174
20 0.996	**21** 0.819	**22** 0.574	**23** 0.087
24 0.998	**25** 0.978	**26** 0.914	**27** 0.839
28 0.559	**29** 0.326	**30** 0.035	

The cosine ratio can be used in right-angled triangles to find

a the length of the side *adjacent* to a given angle if the length of the hypotenuse is known
b the size of an angle if the length of the hypotenuse and the length of the side *adjacent* to this angle are known.

Example 16

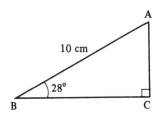

Find the length of BC.

BC is the side adjacent to 28°;
AB is the hypotenuse.

ratio $\dfrac{\text{length of adjacent}}{\text{length of hypotenuse}} = \cos 28°$

so, $\dfrac{BC}{AB} = \cos 28° = 0.883$

$\dfrac{BC}{10} = 0.883$

Multiply both sides by 10

$BC = 0.883 \times 10 = 8.83$

Hence BC is 8.83 cm long.

Exercise 5.14

For each triangle, find the length of BC.

1

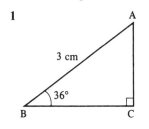

2

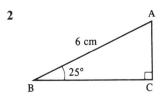

3

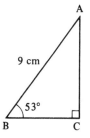

4

5

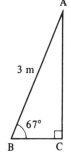

6

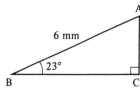

7

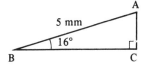

8

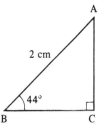

9

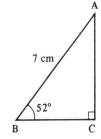

10

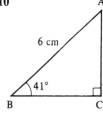

Example 17

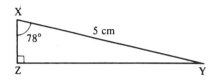

Find the length of XZ.

XZ is the side adjacent to 78°;
XY is the hypotenuse.

ratio $\dfrac{\text{length of adjacent}}{\text{length of hypotenuse}} = \cos 78°$

so, $\dfrac{XZ}{XY} = \cos 78° = 0.208$

$\dfrac{XZ}{5} = 0.208$

Multiply both sides by 5

$XZ = 0.208 \times 5 = 1.040$

Hence XZ is 1.04 cm long.

Exercise 5.15

For each triangle, find the length of XZ.

1
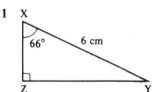

2
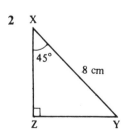

3
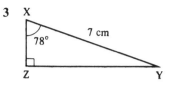

4
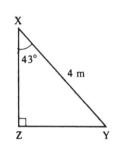

5 **6**
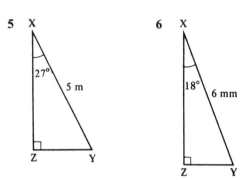

7
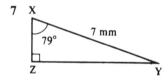

8
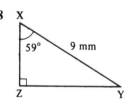

9 **10**
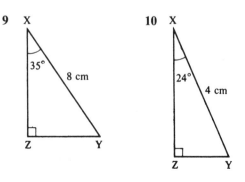

Example 18

A flagpole is supported by wires 15.6 m long which meet the ground at an angle of 62°.

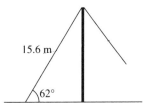

How far from the base of the pole are the wires fixed to the ground?

The wire, flagpole and ground form a right-angled triangle. If we let x represent the distance from the base of the wire to the base of the flagpole we have

$$\frac{x}{15.6} = \cos 62° = 0.469$$

$$\frac{x}{15.6} = 0.469$$

Multiply both sides by 15.6

$$x = 15.6 \times 0.496 = 7.7376$$

Hence the distance from the base of the wire to the base of the flagpole is 7.7 m (correct to 1 dp).

Exercise 5.16

1 The diagram shows the gang-plank of a boat. It meets the bank at an angle of 34° and is 1.8 m long.

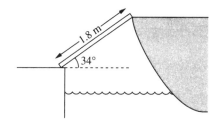

How far is the boat away from the bank?

2 A rectangular framework has been made with straws. The diagonal straw is 12 cm long and meets the base of the framework at an angle of 41°.

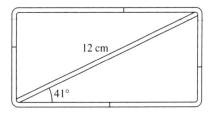

How wide is the framework?

3 Mumbles is 20 km on a bearing of 310° from Porthcawl. A ship sails west from Porthcawl until it is due south of Mumbles.

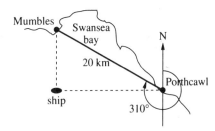

How far has the ship sailed?

4 A lean-to shed has a roof 2.2 m wide which slopes at an angle of 20° to the horizontal. The width of the shed is shown in the diagram by the letter y.

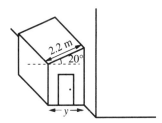

Calculate the value of y.

5 A ramp 1.9 m long is built against a step. The ramp meets the ground at an angle of 15°.

How far is the edge of the ramp from the base of the step?

6 This is a design sketch for a ramp to be built as part of a cycle race track. Each side of the ramp is 3.5 m long and the sides of the ramp meet the ground at an angle of 35°. The width of the ramp is shown in the sketch by the letter *z*.

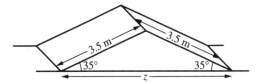

Calculate the value of *z*.

7 This is a sketch of a triangular building plot.

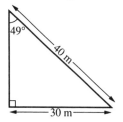

Calculate the area of the building plot.

8 A ladder 2.9 m long rests against a wall.
The foot of the ladder makes an angle of 68° with the ground.

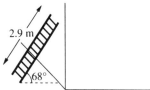

How far is the foot of the ladder from the base of the wall?

9 A step ladder with legs 2.5 m long is standing with each leg making an angle of 80° with the floor.

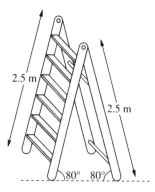

What is the distance between the feet of the step ladder?

10 Vicki and Emma are both flying kites.
Vicki is flying hers on a 50 m string and Emma is flying hers on a 60 m string.
The kites collide when Vicki's string makes an angle of 60° with the ground and Emma's string makes an angle of 46° with the ground.

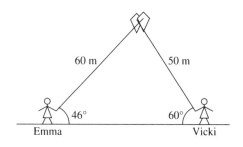

How far apart are Vicki and Emma when the kites collide?

Example 19

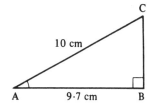

Find the size of $\widehat{A}$.

AB is the side adjacent to the required angle, $\widehat{A}$; AC is the hypotenuse.

ratio $\dfrac{\text{length of adjacent}}{\text{length of hypotenuse}} = \cos A$

so, $\cos A = \dfrac{AB}{AC} = \dfrac{9.7}{10} = 0.97$

$\cos A = 0.97$

From the table of cosines on page 66, the size of the angle whose cosine is 0.97 is 14°.

Hence $\widehat{A} = 14°$.

Exercise 5.17

For each triangle, find the size of $\widehat{A}$.

1
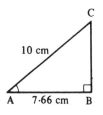

2
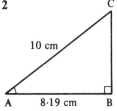

3
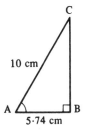

4
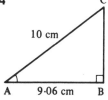

5
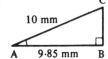

6
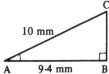

7
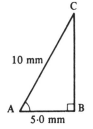

8
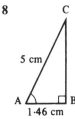

9
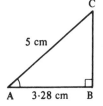

10

Example 20

Find the size of $\widehat{Z}$.

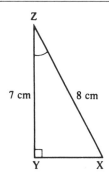

YZ is the side adjacent to $\widehat{Z}$;
XZ is the hypotenuse.

ratio $\dfrac{\text{length of adjacent}}{\text{length of hypotenuse}} = \cos Z$

so, $\cos Z = \dfrac{YZ}{XZ} = \dfrac{7}{8} = 0.875$

$\cos Z = 0.875$

From the table of cosines on page 66, the size of the angle whose cosine is 0.875 is 29°.

Hence $\widehat{Z} = 29°$.

Exercise 5.18

For each triangle, find the size of $\widehat{Z}$.

1
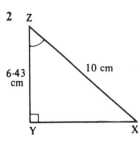

2

3
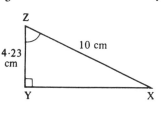

4
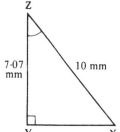

5

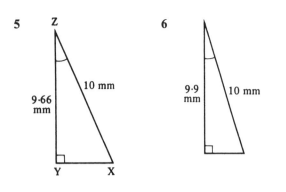

6

$$\cos X = \frac{3.4}{15.6} = 0.218 \ \text{(correct to 3 dp)}$$

$$\cos X = 0.218$$

Hence the angle between the wire and the ground is $77°$ (correct to the nearest degree.)

7 **8**

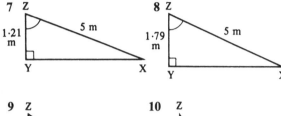

Exercise 5.19

1 This diagram shows the gang-plank of a boat. It is 1.8 m long and the boat is 0.8 m from the bank.

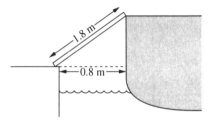

At what angle does the gang-plank meet the bank?

9 **10**

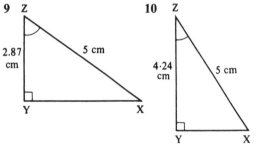

2 A rectangular framework 12 cm by 9 cm has been made with straws. The diagonal straw is 15 cm long.

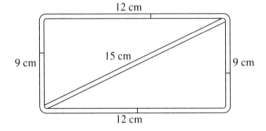

What is the angle between the diagonal straw and one of the 12 cm straws?

3 The direct distance from Lincoln to Worksop is 40 km. Worksop is 38 km to the west of Lincoln.

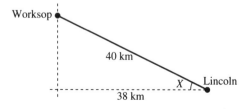

a Find the angle marked X on the diagram.
b Find the bearing of Lincoln from Worksop.

Example 21

A flagpole is supported by wires 15.6 m long which meet the ground 3.4 m from the base of the pole.

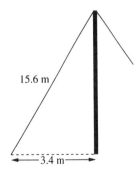

At what angle do the wires meet the ground?

The wire, flagpole and ground form a right-angled triangle. If we let X represent the angle at which the wires meet the ground we have

4 A lean-to shed has a roof 2.7 m wide. The shed itself is 2.16 m wide.

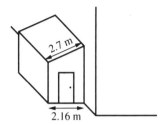

Find the angle at which the shed roof slopes.

5 A ramp 1.9 m long is built against a step. The edge of the ramp is 1.7 m from the base of the step.

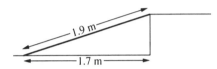

Find the angle at which the ramp slopes.

6 This is a design sketch for a ramp to be built as part of a cycle race track. It has two equal sloping sides 2.4 m long. It is 3.6 m wide.

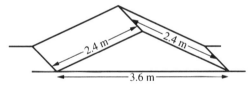

Find the angle between one sloping side of the ramp and the ground.

7 This is a sketch of a triangular building plot with an area of 1400 m².

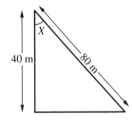

a Find the size of the angle marked *X* on the diagram.
b Find the length of the third side of the building plot.

8 A ladder 2.9 m long rests against a wall. The foot of the ladder is 0.7 m from the wall.

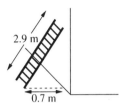

Find the angle the foot of the ladder makes with the ground.

9 A step ladder with legs 2.5 m long is standing with the feet of its legs 0.8 m apart.

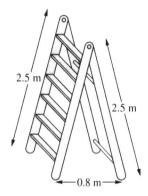

What is the angle between the legs of the step ladder and the floor?

10 Vicki and Emma are both flying kites on 70 m strings. The kites collide when Vicki and Emma are 24 m apart.

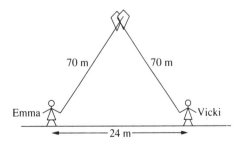

What angles do the kite strings make with the ground when they collide?

Using tangents

The table on the right gives the tangent ratio of any angle T° from 0° to 90°.

Example 22

Find the tangent ratio for

a 24°   **b** 79°

a tan 24° = 0.445
b tan 79° = 5.14

Example 23

Find the angle whose tangent ratio is

a 0.287   **b** 2.36

a tan 16° = 0.287, so the size of the angle is 16°
b tan 67° = 2.36, so the size of the angle is 67°

Note that the tangent ratio gets larger and larger until tan 90° = infinity (∞).

Exercise 5.20

Find the tangent ratio of the following angles.

1	30°	**2**	10°	**3**	15°	**4**	35°
5	17°	**6**	28°	**7**	39°	**8**	42°
9	45°	**10**	50°	**11**	65°	**12**	69°
13	74°	**14**	76°	**15**	80°		

Find the size of the angle for the following tangent ratios.

16	0.364	**17**	0.839	**18**	0.087	**19**	0.466
20	0.249	**21**	0.424	**22**	0.754	**23**	0.869
24	1.43	**25**	1.73	**26**	2.75	**27**	3.27
28	3.73	**29**	4.33	**30**	5.14		

The tangent ratio can be used in right-angled triangles to find

a the length of the side opposite to a given angle if the length of the adjacent side is known
b the size of an angle if the lengths of the side opposite to this angle and of the side adjacent to this angle are known.

Table of tangents

T°	tan T	T°	tan T
0	0.000	45	1.00
1	0.017	46	1.04
2	0.035	47	1.07
3	0.052	48	1.11
4	0.070	49	1.15
5	0.087	50	1.19
6	0.105	51	1.23
7	0.123	52	1.28
8	0.141	53	1.33
9	0.158	54	1.38
10	0.176	55	1.43
11	0.194	56	1.48
12	0.213	57	1.54
13	0.231	58	1.60
14	0.249	59	1.66
15	0.268	60	1.73
16	0.287	61	1.80
17	0.306	62	1.88
18	0.325	63	1.96
19	0.344	64	2.05
20	0.364	65	2.14
21	0.384	66	2.25
22	0.404	67	2.36
23	0.424	68	2.48
24	0.445	69	2.61
25	0.466	70	2.75
26	0.488	71	2.90
27	0.510	72	3.08
28	0.532	73	3.27
29	0.554	74	3.49
30	0.577	75	3.73
31	0.601	76	4.01
32	0.625	77	4.33
33	0.649	78	4.70
34	0.675	79	5.14
35	0.700	80	5.67
36	0.727	81	6.31
37	0.754	82	7.12
38	0.781	83	8.14
39	0.810	84	9.51
40	0.839	85	11.4
41	0.869	86	14.3
42	0.900	87	19.1
43	0.933	88	28.6
44	0.966	89	57.3
		90	∞

Example 24

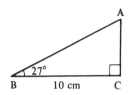

Find the length of AC.

AC is the side opposite to 27°;
BC is the side adjacent to 27°.

ratio $\dfrac{\text{length of opposite}}{\text{length of adjacent}} = \tan 27°$

so, $\quad \dfrac{AC}{BC} = \tan 27° = 0.510$

$\dfrac{AC}{10} = 0.510$

Multiply both sides by 10

$\quad AC = 0.510 \times 10 = 5.10$

Hence AC is 5.1 cm long.

Exercise 5.21

For each triangle, find the length of AC.

1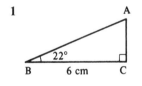

2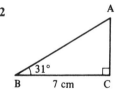

3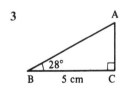

4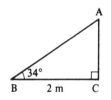

5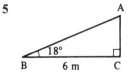

6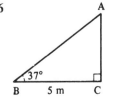

7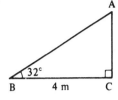

8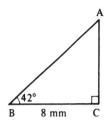

9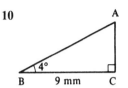

10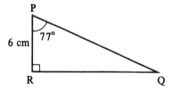

Example 25

Find the length of QR. Give your answer to the nearest centimetre.

QR is the side opposite to 77°;
PR is the side adjacent to 77°.

ratio $\dfrac{\text{length of opposite}}{\text{length of adjacent}} = \tan 77°$

so, $\quad \dfrac{QR}{PR} = \tan 77° = 4.33$

$\dfrac{QR}{6} = 4.33$

Multiply both sides by 6

$\quad QR = 4.33 \times 6 = 25.98$

Hence QR is 26 cm long, to the nearest centimetre.

76

Exercise 5.22

For each triangle, find the length of QR.

1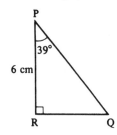

2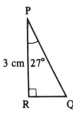

3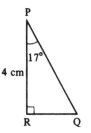

4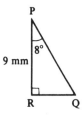

5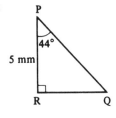

6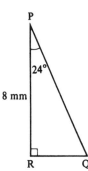

7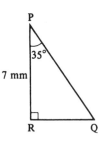

8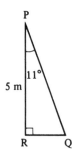

9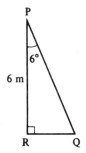

10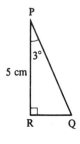

Example 26

If the angle of elevation of the sun is 65°, how high is a flagpole which casts a shadow 15 m long?

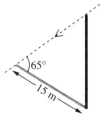

The sun's rays, the flagpole and ground form a right-angled triangle. If we let x represent the height of the flagpole, we have

$$\frac{x}{15} = \tan 65° = 2.14$$

$$\frac{x}{15} = 2.14$$

Multiply both sides by 15

$$x = 15 \times 2.14 = 32.1$$

Hence the flagpole is 32.1 m high.

Exercise 5.23

1 When the angle of elevation of the sun is 56°, a tower casts a shadow 32 m long.

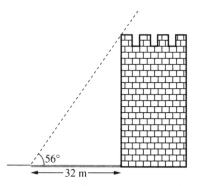

Find the height of the tower.

2 The foot of a ladder is 2.1 m from the base of a wall and makes an angle of 67° with the ground.

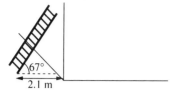

How far up the wall does the ladder reach?

3 A man 1.8 m tall is standing 32 m from the base of a cliff looking up through an angle of elevation of 49° at a gull's nest.

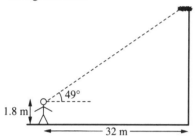

How high up the cliff is the gull's nest?

4 A boat leaves a harbour and sails on a bearing of 075° until it is 50 km to the north of the harbour.

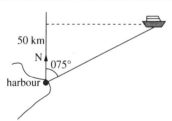

How far is the ship to the east of the harbour?

5 The legs of a step ladder make an angle of 72° with the floor when they are opened to a gap of 0.7 m.

How high is the top of the step ladder when the legs are in this position?

6 The sail of a boat is a triangle with a base of 4.4 m and base angles of 60° and 90°.

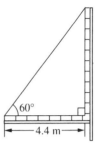

Find the height of the sail.

7 A plane takes off and climbs at an angle of 46°. It passes directly over a house 1.2 km from the point of take off.

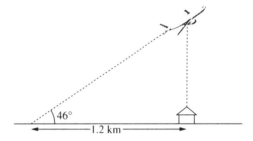

How high is the plane when it passes over the house?

8 A wheelchair ramp 3.7 m long with a slope of 10° is needed to get up a step.

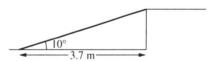

How high is the step?

9 A roof has two equal sides which slope at an angle of 34° to the horizontal. The whole roof is 8 m wide.

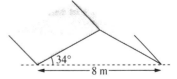

How high is the centre of the roof above the edge of the roof?

10 This diagram shows a building plot.

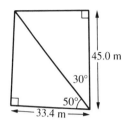

Find the area of the building plot.

Example 27

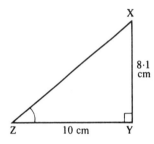

Find the size of $\widehat{Z}$.

XY is the side opposite to the required angle, $\widehat{Z}$; YZ is the side adjacent to the required angle, $\widehat{Z}$.

ratio $\dfrac{\text{length of opposite}}{\text{length of adjacent}} = \tan Z$

so, $\tan Z = \dfrac{XY}{YZ} = \dfrac{8.1}{10} = 0.81$

$\tan Z = 0.81$

From the table of tangents on page 74, the size of the angle whose tangent is 0.81 is 39°.

Hence $\widehat{Z} = 39°$.

Exercise 5.24

For each triangle, find the size of Z.

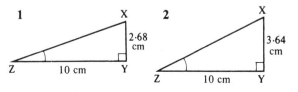

3

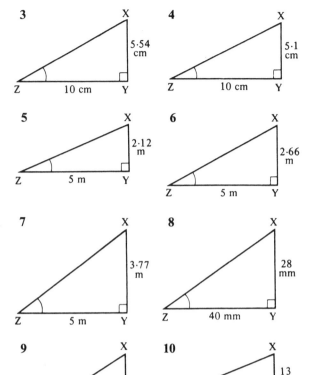

5

6

7

8

9

10

Example 28

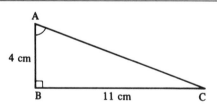

Find the size of $\widehat{A}$.

BC is the side opposite to the required angle, $\widehat{A}$; AB is the side adjacent to the required angle, $\widehat{A}$.

ratio $\dfrac{\text{length of opposite}}{\text{length of adjacent}} = \tan A$

so, $\tan A = \dfrac{BC}{AB} = \dfrac{11}{4} = 2.75$

From the table of tangents on page 74, the size of the angle whose tangent is 2.75 is 70°

Hence $\widehat{A} = 70°$.

Exercise 5.25

For each triangle, find the size of A.

1

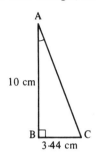

10 cm

3·44 cm

2

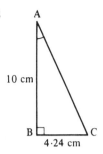

10 cm

4·24 cm

3

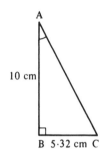

10 cm

B 5·32 cm C

4

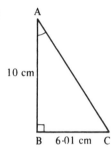

10 cm

B 6·01 cm C

5

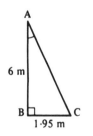

6 m

1·95 m

6

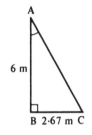

6 m

B 2·67 m C

7

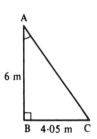

6 m

B 4·05 m C

8

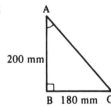

200 mm

B 180 mm C

9

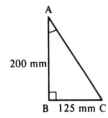

200 mm

B 125 mm C

10

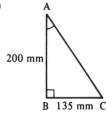

200 mm

B 135 mm C

Example 29

A flagpole 23 m high casts a shadow 15 m long.

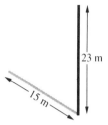

23 m

15 m

What is the angle of elevation of the sun?

The sun's rays, the flagpole and ground form a right-angled triangle. If we let X represent the angle of elevation of the sun, we have

$$\tan X = \frac{23}{15} = 1.53 \text{ (correct to 2 dp)}$$

$$\tan X = 1.53 \text{ (correct to 2 dp)}$$

$$X = 57° \text{ (correct to the nearest degree)}$$

Hence the angle of elevation of the sun is 57°.

Exercise 5.26

1 A tower 43 m high casts a shadow 32 m long.

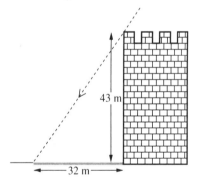

43 m

32 m

Find the angle of elevation of the sun.

2 The foot of a ladder is 2.1 m from the base of a wall and the ladder reaches 6.4 m up the wall.

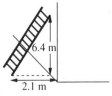

6.4 m

2.1 m

What angle does the foot of the ladder make with the ground?

3 A man 1.8 metres tall is standing 32 m from the base of a cliff looking up at a gull's nest which is 17 m high.

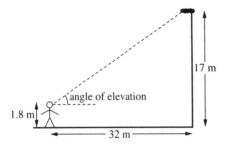

What is the angle of elevation of the gull's nest from the man?

4 A boat leaves a harbour and sails to a position 50 km to the north and 85 km to the east of the harbour.

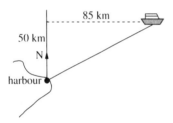

What is the bearing of the ship from the harbour?

5 The top of a step ladder is 2.7 m high when the legs are opened to a gap of 0.9 m.

What angle do the legs make with the floor when they are in this position?

6 The sail of a boat is a triangle with a base of 4.4 m and a height of 6.3 m.
One of the base angles of the sail is 90°.

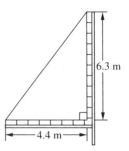

What is the size of the other base angle?

7 A plane takes off and climbs in a straight line. It is 0.6 km high when it passes directly over a house 1.2 km from the point of take off.

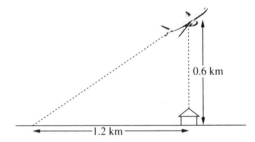

At what angle to the horizontal did the plane climb?

8 A wheelchair ramp 2.8 m long is needed to get up a step 0.4 m high.

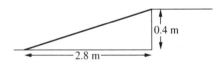

What angle does the ramp make with the horizontal?

9 A roof with equal sides is 8 m wide and is 3 m high in the centre.

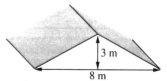

What angle do the sides of the roof make with the horizontal?

10 This diagram shows a building plot.

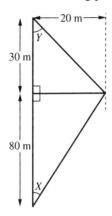

Find the angles marked *X* and *Y*.

3

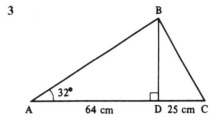

4

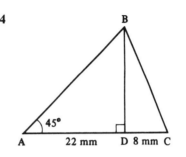

Exercise 5.27

In questions **1** to **4**, find
a the length of BD
b the size of angle C.

1

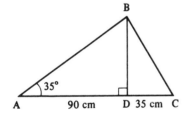

2

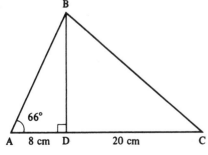

In questions **5** to **7**, find
a the length of QS
b the size of angle R.

5

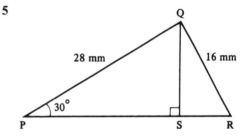

6

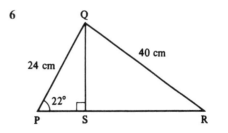

7

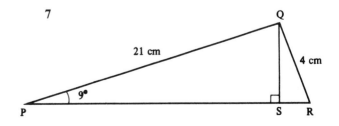

In questions **8** to **10**, find
a the length of XZ
b the size of angle ZXY.

8

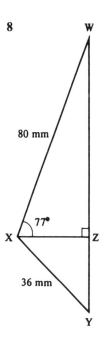

9

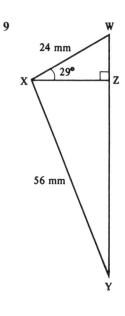

10

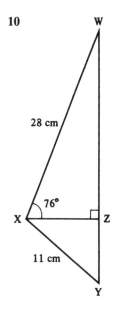

11 The kite string makes an angle of 50° with the ground.
Find the vertical height of the kite above the ground.

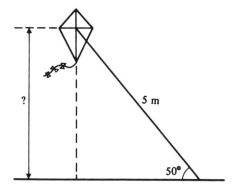

12 The sloping roof of a lean-to shed is 1.5 m in length and it makes an angle of 20° with the horizontal.
Find the distance that it projects from the wall.

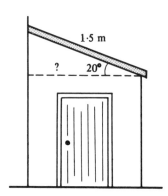